Boys

Poisonous amphibians and
reptiles: recognition,
and bite treatment

12-82

Poisonous Amphibians
And Reptiles

Poisonous Amphibians And Reptiles

RECOGNITION, AND BITE TREATMENT

By

FLOYD BOYS, M.D.

Associate Professor of Health Education
University of Illinois
Urbana, Illinois

And

HOBART M. SMITH, Ph.D.

Professor of Zoology (Herpetology)
University of Illinois
Urbana, Illinois

CHARLES C THOMAS • PUBLISHER
Springfield • Illinois • U.S.A.

CHARLES C THOMAS • PUBLISHER

BANNERSTONE HOUSE

301-327 East Lawrence Avenue, Springfield, Illinois, U.S.A.

Published simultaneously in the British Commonwealth of Nations by
BLACKWELL SCIENTIFIC PUBLICATIONS, LTD., OXFORD, ENGLAND

Published simultaneously in Canada by
THE RYERSON PRESS, TORONTO

© *1959 by* CHARLES C THOMAS • PUBLISHER

Library of Congress Catalog Card Number 58-12149

Printed in the United States of America

PREFACE

The present account of venomous reptiles and amphibians is restricted in scope to those species inhabiting the United States and Canada. Much of the basic information reviewed is applicable to situations existing in other parts of the world, but it is of importance to emphasize that our primary concern is with the problems existing in North America.

It is recognized that in the geographic area with which we are here primarily concerned, the United States, relatively few persons in their lifetime will ever be exposed to the immediate danger of being bitten by a snake of any kind, and that, statistically speaking, the first aid problem of snake bite is not particularly significant. However, since an individual bitten by a poisonous snake is in serious danger of death, the problem becomes one of great personal importance to any individual so victimized.

Although the primary intent of this treatise is to discuss snakes, since these animals include most of the commonly encountered poisonous vertebrates, a general and brief survey of other poisonous animals is included in order to place snakes and their significance as venomous animals in proper perspective.

This summary is necessarily introductory and incomplete. Its perusal, nevertheless, should assist interested students in looking up more detailed supplementary reading, and in becoming better versed about the more *practical* facts relating to first aid procedure in snake bite cases. It is believed that the material presented is accurate as far as it goes, and that, in its synthesis of zoological and medical approaches, it represents a unique contribution to the extensive literature of this field.

ACKNOWLEDGMENTS

We are very grateful to two of the best qualified practitioners of snakebite treatment, Drs. Sherman A. Minton and Frederick A. Shannon, for critical reading of the medical section of this monograph, Part IX. To Mrs. Eleanor E. Buckley we are indebted for the privilege of pre-publication examination of abstracts of the papers appearing in the AAAS volume, *Venoms*, published in late 1956. Bibliographical assistance by Miss Clara Mechel, and by Miss Elizabeth Adkins, is gratefully acknowledged. Thanks are also to be expressed to Miss Alice Boatright and Mr. Lawrence D. Siler for doing part of the illustrative work.

F.B.
H.M.S.

CONTENTS

Page

Preface v

Acknowledgments vii

PART I

Taxonomy (Classification) of Venomous Animals....... 3
  A. Meaning of the Terms Venomous and Poisonous.. 3
  B. Occurrence of Poisons in Animals.............. 4
    1. Invertebrates 4
    2. Vertebrates 4
  C. Classification of Amphibians and Reptiles........ 5
    1. Amphibians 5
    2. Reptiles 5

PART II

Poisonous Amphibia (Salamanders, Frogs, Toads)...... 7
  A. Location of Poison.......................... 7
  B. Modes of Poisoning.......................... 7
  C. Nature of Poison............................ 8
  D. Poisonous Species of North America........... 9
    1. Toads 10
    2. Red-legged Frogs 10
  E. Recognition of this Emergency................ 11
  F. First Aid Treatment.......................... 11

PART III

Poisonous Chelonia (Turtles)........................ 12
  A. Poisonous Species............................ 12

B. Nature of the Poison...................... 13
C. Recognition of this Emergency............... 13
D. First Aid Treatment...................... 14

PART IV

Venomous Lacertilia (Lizards)..................... 15
  A. Kinds of Venomous Lizards in the United States.. 15
  B. Mode of Envenomation...................... 16
  C. Action of the Venom...................... 16
  D. Recognition of this Emergency............... 17
  E. First Aid Treatment...................... 17
  F. Medical Treatment 19

PART V

Venomous Ophidia (Snakes)...................... 21
  A. General Zoological Characteristics of the
     Suborder Ophidia 21
    1. Size 21
    2. Skeletal System 21
    3. Locomotion 22
    4. Skin 22
    5. Rattles 23
    6. Teeth 25
    7. Ears 30
    8. Eyes 30
    9. Tongue 31
   10. Pits 32
   11. Body Temperature 32
   12. Respiration 32
   13. Bladder 32
   14. Copulation and Breeding.................. 33
   15. Diet 33

16. Catching Their Prey...................... 34
17. Deglutition (Swallowing Mechanism)........ 34
18. Erroneous Beliefs About Snakes............ 35
B. Venomous Snakes in the United States........... 39
   1. Kinds of Venomous Snakes................ 39
   2. Proportion of Deadly to Non-Deadly Snakes
      in the United States.................... 41
   3. Mode of Envenomation................... 43
   4. Mode of Spread of Venom................ 44
   5. Composition of Snake Venoms............. 45
   6. Over-all Actions of Venoms............... 48
   7. Potency of the Venomous Bite............. 54
   8. Cause of Deaths from Snakebite........... 59
   9. After-Effects in Survivors from Snakebite.... 60

PART VI

General Precautions Against Snakebites................ 61
A. Season of the Year............................ 61
B. Time of the Day.............................. 61
C. Danger of Snake Den Areas.................... 62
D. Observational Precautions 62
E. Importance of Companions..................... 63
F. Value of Wearing Protective Garments.......... 64
G. Snakebite Kits................................ 64
   1. Tourniquet 66
   2. Antiseptic 67
   3. Cutting Instrument 67
   4. Suction Cups 68
H. Artificial Bodily Immunity Against Venom....... 69
I. Control 70

PART VII

Recognition of Poisonous Snakes and Their Bites....... 72
A. Examination of the Snake...................... 72
    1. Front Fangs 72
    2. Pits 73
    3. Rattles 73
    4. Skin Color Patterns...................... 73
    5. Scale Pattern on the Under-Surface of Tail.. 81
    6. Shape of Head.......................... 81
    7. Snake Noises........................... 83
B. Examination of the Bitten Person.............. 83
    1. Bite Pattern............................ 84
    2. Pain 85
    3. Swelling 86
    4. Miscellaneous Symptoms 87

PART VIII

First Aid Measures in Treating Poisonous and
    Non-Poisonous Snakebite Cases 88
A. Keeping Bodily Metabolism at a Minimum....... 88
    1. Position 88
    2. Muscular Activity....................... 89
    3. Fear and Emotional Excitement............ 89
    4. Alcohol 89
    5. Food 89
B. Mechanical Removal of Venom from the
    Subcutaneous Tissues 90
    1. Tourniquet 92
    2. Multiple Incisions 93
    3. Suction 96
C. Sending for Medical Assistance................. 98

D. Recommended General First Aid Procedure in
   Specific Case Situations 99
   1. The Victim Is Alone..................... 99
   2. The Victim Has One Companion.......... 101
   3. The Victim Has Two or More Companions.. 103

PART IX

Medical Treatment in Cases of Snakebite............... 106
A. General Recommendations (Summary).......... 110
B. Continuation of Standard First Aid Measures..... 111
C. Antivenins 114
D. Anti-Shock Measures 121
   1. General Measures 122
   2. Blood Transfusion....................... 122
   3. Other Intravenous Injections............... 123
   4. Miscellaneous Drugs..................... 123
E. Calcium Supplements 125
F. Glycine 126
G. Neostigmine 126
H. Ascorbic Acid 127
I. Sedation 127
J. Artificial Respiration......................... 128
K. Antibiotics 129
L. Purgatives 129
M. Antipruritics 130
N. Diet and Liquids............................ 130
O. Cryotherapy (Local Tissue Refrigeration)....... 130
P. Continued Care 131

Bibliography 132

Postscript 143

Index 145

Poisonous Amphibians
And Reptiles

PART I

TAXONOMY (CLASSIFICATION) OF VENOMOUS ANIMALS

A. MEANING OF THE TERMS *VENOMOUS* AND *POISONOUS*

A *venomous* animal is one possessing venoms of one or more kinds. A venom is a body fluid that contains one or more poisonous ingredients, and that is used primarily in exploitation of its deadly properties. Most animal venoms are highly complex, containing numerous poisonous as well as harmless biochemical fractions. Venoms are sometimes used aggressively, for the most part by biting, scratching, and stinging, and sometimes they are used passively, as for example the venomous hairs on certain caterpillars.

A *poisonous* animal is one that produces a poison by normal bodily processes. A poison is defined as any substance chemically producing an injurious or deadly effect when introduced into an organism. All venomous reptiles, including certain snakes as well as one species of lizard, are properly referred to as poisonous, since their venoms contain one or more poisons. Many other vertebrates, however, possess no venom as such, but are still poisonous, having body fluids which prove noxious when ingested by other animals. It may thus be said that all venomous animals are poisonous, but that not all poisonous animals are venomous. So far as snakes are concerned, either term is appropriate. The two are used interchangeably in this work. Nevertheless, the term venomous is more strictly accurate

3

for the poisonous snakes and lizards, and is thus, other factors being equal, the more preferable of the two terms.

B. OCCURRENCE OF POISONS IN ANIMALS

1. Invertebrates

Almost every phylum of invertebrates contains one or more species of animals poisonous in one way or another. Familiar examples are certain ticks, spiders, scorpions, flies, leeches, earthworms, jellyfish, beetles, wasps, bees, centipedes, and anemones.

2. Vertebrates

In all classes of vertebrates (birds excepted), certain species possess poison of some sort. Reptiles rank at the top of the list primarily because they include snakes, many species of which are notoriously venomous. Amphibians come next, followed in order by fishes and mammals. Venom is found among mammals in the saliva of shrews, and also is associated with the spur on the hind legs of the male of one primitive Australian mammal (duckbilled platypus). Venomous fishes include certain rays and catfishes, which possess bony spines associated with venom sacs in the skin.

A few vertebrates are known to be poisonous if eaten, but they are not venomous. A number of sharks, rays, ratfish, and bony fishes, both marine and freshwater, are poisonous when eaten. So also are marine turtles in certain regions. The liver of certain seals and bears is deadly poisonous, apparently because of a high concentration of vitamin A (Halstead, 1956: 23). The latter author provides an impressive account of the symptoms and treatment for all known poisonous marine animals. There is an astonishing and sobering array of animals dangerous to use as food.

C. CLASSIFICATION OF AMPHIBIANS AND REPTILES

1. Amphibians

Three orders of living amphibians are recognized:

a. Order APODA—legless, earthwormlike animals (caecilians).

Of no interest to First Aiders. These amphibians are not seen in North America.

b. Order CAUDATA—tailed, and with 2-4 legs (salamanders, newts).

Of no importance to First Aiders in the Western Hemisphere, because no species has a significantly strong skin poison. Some Eurasian forms do have powerful epidermal secretions.

c. Order ANURA—no tail, always 4 legs (frogs, toads).

Many anurans have a strong skin poison capable of affecting humans. These shall be discussed later.

2. Reptiles

Living reptiles represent four orders:

a. Order RHYNCHOCEPHALIA—the tuatara (a lizardlike animal) of New Zealand, the sole survivor of this Order.

This creature is of no interest to First Aiders as the reptile is not encountered in North America, and is not venomous.

b. Order CHELONIA—turtles, terrapins, and tortoises.

No venom occurs in chelonians, although bites may be mechanically and infectiously dangerous. A very few species are dangerous through possession of a poisonous property to be discussed later.

c. Order CROCODILIA — crocodiles, alligators, and caimans.

Most First Aiders will never be called upon to treat people bitten by members of this Order. Bites by these animals are dangerous mainly because of the dirty, severe wounds they may produce. In such rare instances, a First Aider would have to treat for massive hemorrhage, severe shock, etc. No venomous material *per se* is introduced into the victim.

d. Order SQUAMATA—a group containing four suborders, three of which are still in existence.

Suborder LACERTILIA—lizards

The only member of this group in the world which First Aiders need be specifically concerned with, except for certain large species producing lacerations by their teeth, is the famed Gila Monster of Western North America. This species is discussed further in Part IV.

Suborder OPHIDIA—snakes

These reptiles are the most important animals for the First Aiders to study, as certain snakes constitute the bulk of venomous creatures known to attack and poison humans. Most of the following discussion pertains to this group.

Suborder AMPHISBAENIA—worm lizards

Of no interest to First Aiders. These animals are restricted to tropical and subtropical regions of the world, occurring in the United States only in Florida. They are not venomous, and are too small to bite humans painfully.

PART II

POISONOUS AMPHIBIA
(Salamanders, Frogs, Toads)

A. LOCATION OF POISON

In all amphibians a certain amount of poison is present in the skin secretion. The amount is totally inconsequential in most species, so far as humans are concerned; most Anurans (i.e., frogs) are properly regarded as an excellent source of food.

Yet in some species the skin secretion contains one or more poisons fatal to humans as well as to other predators. Only the skin secretion is poisonous, however; no species can inflict more than superficial mechanical damage by other means (biting, scratching).

Most species having a dangerous skin poison also have a warty skin. The "warts" are aggregations of poison glands. Some deadly poisonous species are smooth-skinned, however.

B. MODES OF POISONING

Since the venom in all amphibians, where present, is passively held in the skin, an animal can be poisoned by an amphibian only through aggressive behavior by the victimized animal. So far as humans are concerned, the poison can be acquired either by (1) carelessly rubbing the skin of poisonous amphibians against areas of human skin where cuts or abrasions are present, or by (2) swallowing the whole animal or any part of it on which the skin remains or has been rubbed. The poisons are effective either directly through the blood stream (as it enters cuts in the skin) or indirectly through the digestive tract from which it is absorbed secondarily into the blood stream. In either case, the harmful effects are mediated entirely through the circulatory system.

C. NATURE OF POISON

The primary poisons found in the skin of amphibians are of two sorts: (1) epinephrine-like substances (similar to adrenalin), which accelerate heart rate and breathing, and (2) digitalis-like substances, which retard breathing and diminish heart rate at the same time strengthening the beat. In addition to these effects, typical symptoms of amphibian poisoning include vomiting, partial paralysis, and, in fatal cases, death from cardiac arrest of various types according to the relative concentrations of the two sorts of poisons. Minute quantities of either substance can cause death of humans as well as of other animals. Epinephrine is quickly absorbed in the mouth, but is destroyed in the stomach. On the contrary, the digitaloids are not absorbed in the mouth, but instead are absorbed through the stomach.

The potency of the poisons of the few species of amphibians possessing them in well-developed form should not be underestimated. In Central America one tiny frog has a skin secretion so powerful that natives use it for poison on the tips of hunting arrows. The lethal effect is almost instantaneous. Cases are on record of humans having died from eating poisonous toads mistaken for edible bullfrogs. There is little likelihood of such deaths occurring in North America where both types of amphibians are native, well-known, and usually not confused. It is surprising, however, that more toddling children have not been killed by innocently popping a toad into their mouths; the hazard exists especially in less civilized regions but merits recognition everywhere dangerously venomous amphibians are known.

D. POISONOUS SPECIES OF NORTH AMERICA

Toads, and red-colored frogs of two species, are known to be dangerous to man in North America (Fig. 1).

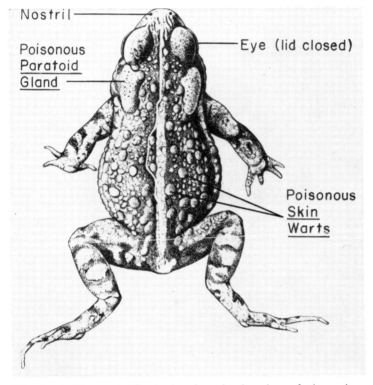

Nostril

Poisonous
Paratoid
Gland

Eye (lid closed)

Poisonous
Skin
Warts

Fig. 1. A Common Toad, showing the location of the poison glands. (Adapted from Malcolm Smith.)

1. Toads

Toads are found in almost all the temperate and tropical parts of the world, and in virtually all parts of the United States. They vary in body length from ¾ to 8 inches; the Marine Toad of southern United States and tropical America, and the Colorado River Toad of Arizona, are among the largest species of the world. Toads may be recognized by the fat body, relatively short legs, warty skin, occurrence often far from water, and, most importantly, a large skin gland (the *parotoid gland*) located just back of the eye. The warts and the parotoid glands are the primary sources of the skin poisons.

2. Red-legged Frogs

Two frogs, one found in western and one in eastern United States, possess a skin poison that may be dangerous to man. Each has a conspicuous red coloration concealed as the frog is seen in the normal sitting position. When the hind legs are outstretched, the red is easily seen on the legs themselves and on the rear sides of the body.

These frogs are found in or near water, and are smooth-skinned like other frogs. They reach a snout-vent length of about 4-5 inches, and could conceivably be confused with edible species with which they occur abundantly in some areas. No cases are known of human consumption of these red-legged frogs, but effects of the skin poison upon other animals suggest that humans should avoid poisoning by this species.

All other Anurans of North America are presumably safe for human consumption, although care should be exercised with some of the small warty tree frogs, and some toad-like, warty, burrowing species. In all cases of doubt, if the frog must be eaten, care should be taken to avoid contamination of the edible parts through direct contact with the outer surface of the animal's skin or with anything else (such as the hands) having come in contact with the skin. The subcutaneous tissues themselves are not poisonous.

E.   RECOGNITION OF THIS EMERGENCY

In typical cases of poisoning by amphibians, the following facts will be ascertained. (1) The victim has handled a terrestrial, warty TOAD, or a RED-COLORED FROG, in some manner as described above. (2) Within a few minutes of this handling, the human victim becomes sick, and the bodily physiological reactions mentioned above appear and become progressively worse.

F.   FIRST AID TREATMENT

(1) Use of emetics (drugs that produce vomiting).
(2) Treatment for shock.
(3) Urgent medical attention for the victim.

PART III

POISONOUS CHELONIA (Turtles)

A. POISONOUS SPECIES

Turtles possess no venom of any sort in the skin, mouth, or elsewhere. Their poisonous properties are derived solely from their food. If they have eaten certain foods poisonous to humans (but not to turtles), the poison may be dispersed for a time in all bodily tissues, including the muscles that humans eat. Thus, humans eating such poisonous tissues are themselves poisoned, not from the turtle itself but from the food eaten by the turtle.

So far as known, the only turtles possessing such secondary poisonous properties are the Eastern Box Turtle of the United States, and certain Sea Turtles of the Western Pacific. The sea turtles presumably obtain their poison by eating certain marine algae. Box Turtles derive theirs from consuming poisonous mushrooms.

The Eastern Box Turtle occurs southward from central Nebraska to the Gulf of Mexico in southern Texas, and eastward to the Atlantic as far north as New England. It is easily recognizable by its high, rounded shell, which can be completely closed below by the hinged, movable halves of the lower part of the shell. The color varies from a nearly uniform straw or brownish color to a radiate pattern of yellow on a dark background.

B. NATURE OF THE POISON

Mushroom poisoning is not so common as it formerly was because most mushrooms offered for the table are cultivated under artificial conditions. *Amanita phalloides* and *Amanita muscaria* are the commonest forms of poisonous mushroom. The former is white or slightly brownish in color. Also the stem is larger than the diameter of the cap, bulges at the base and arises from a sort of cup. The gills are white. *Amanita muscaria* is large, highly colored (yellow, orange and red), and the gills are white.

The poison of the *Amanita phalloides* mushroom has not been fully identified, but it probably is related to the chemical "indole." The symptoms and signs in poisoning by this particular mushroom are first abdominal pain, vomiting, and diarrhea. Later suppression of urine develops due to kidney involvement (nephritis), and finally jaundice occurs due to liver involvement (hepatitis).

The poison of *Amanita muscaria* is due to the chemical "muscarine." The signs and symptoms of muscaria poisoning are similar to the pharmacologic effect of muscarine which affects primarily the nervous system. Mental confusion, dizziness, delirium and convulsions may be expected, as well as sweating, slow pulse, watery stools, rapid respiration and dyspnea (marked shortness of breath).

C. RECOGNITION OF THIS EMERGENCY

In typical cases of poisoning by turtles, the following facts will be ascertained. (1) The victim has eaten Box Turtle meat or soup. (2) The ground area in which the culprit turtle was found grows poisonous mushrooms which might have been eaten. (3) The victim evidences the symptoms and signs known to accompany mushroom poisoning.

D. FIRST AID TREATMENT

(1) Use of emetics (drugs that produce vomiting).

(2) Various supportive measures such as caffeine, brandy. These are mainly for minimization of shock.

(3) Urgent medical attention for the victim. There is no specific antidote for poisoning by *Amanita phalloides*, but for poisoning by *Amanita muscaria* there is a specific antidote, the drug atropine.

PART IV

VENOMOUS LACERTILIA (Lizards)

A. KINDS OF VENOMOUS LIZARDS IN THE UNITED STATES

The only species of venomous lizards in the entire world are the nearly identical Beaded Lizard and the Gila Monster (Fig. 2), which occur from extreme southern

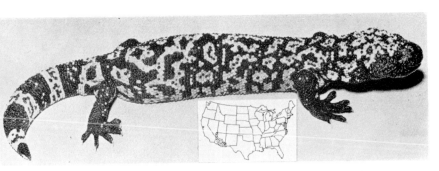

Fig. 2. A Gila Monster and range thereof in the United States. (Adapted from Bogert and Martín del Campo.)

Nevada and Utah southward through Arizona, western New Mexico, and western Mexico. They are fairly large lizards (two feet long, four inches wide) with a heavy body, strong short limbs, and a fat short tail. The skin has a beaded appearance, and is colored black (or brown) and orange (or yellow).

15

B.　MODE OF ENVENOMATION

The venom is secreted by salivary glands (submandibular) at the rear of the lower jaw, and flows out between the lips and the lower teeth. All of the teeth, of which there are about 20 in each jaw (total 40 in the mouth), are strong, curved, and have a deep groove running down the front edge. The only way the venom can get into a bitten victim is by seepage and capillary action along the venom grooves primarily in the teeth of the lower jaw. Thus, Gila Monsters typically bite with a bulldog-like tenacity, allowing plenty of time for the venom to seep into the wounds.

Shannon (1957) states that no single substantiated case of a human death due solely to a Gila Monster bite has been reported despite a great mass of largely lurid literature to the contrary. The low mortality rate is due partly to the relatively inefficient venom-injection apparatus of this lizard, and partly to the free drainage characteristic of its bites. Forcible release of the animal usually augments laceration, producing profuse bleeding that tends to remove much of the venom.

C.　ACTION OF THE VENOM

Gila Monster venom possesses both hemopathic and neurotoxic components. Hemorrhagins present in the venom, especially in cases with badly lacerated wounds, may result in localized bleeding persisting for several hours. The bite is extremely painful, and when large quantities of venom are injected, rapid swelling and edema follow much as in Rattlesnake bite. Neurotoxins, apparently the predominant component, may produce flaccid (limp) paralysis. Gila Monster bite victims not infrequently complain also of tinnitus (ringing in the ears), dysphagia

(painful or difficult swallowing), considerable pain localized around the bite area, and varying degrees of emotional
instability.

Victims of Gila Monster bites are often (not always)
severely sick people. Attending physicians should treat
such cases seriously and hospitalize the victim for clinical
observation and whatever care is necessary. The near-
fatal reactions to the bite of a small Gila Monster ($8\frac{1}{2}$
inches total length) which retained a hold by 5 upper and
2 lower teeth for only 12 to 15 seconds, as described by
Tinkham (1956), are highly impressive. In this case there
were no lacerations or cuts at the site of the bite; clearly
if the venom is not largely removed by such traumatic
means, its effects could be fatal. Loeb (1913) has already
demonstrated that the venom is highly potent.

D. RECOGNITION OF THIS EMERGENCY

In typical cases of poisoning by a Gila Monster, the
following facts will be ascertained. (1) If bitten under
natural conditions, the locale is within the geographic
range of the Gila Monster. (2) If not under natural conditions, the locale is some zoo or other place where live
Gila Monsters are kept. (3) That the victim was bitten
by a lizard answering the general description of the Gila
Monster (local identification is usually unreliable). (4)
That the victim develops the signs and symptoms typical
of poisoning by the Gila Monster.

E. FIRST AID TREATMENT

After disengaging the jaws, the following first aid
measures are recommended:

1. For the same reasons mentioned in connection with
treatment of poisonous snakebite cases (see Part VIII,

Section A), a primary precaution in Gila Monster bites is to keep bodily metabolism at a minimum. To do this, the victim should lie down in the immediate territory where bitten, usually in a comfortable spot where he can be protected from sun or rain. Further, he should avoid all exertion, and should not consume any alcohol or other metabolic stimulant.

2. As in standard snakebite first aid treatment (see Part VIII, Section B-1), it is also advisable to apply a tourniquet a few inches above the Gila Monster bite area. The tourniquet need not be tight; it should be just constrictive enough to retard the flow of venom-carrying lymph in the subcutaneous tissues as the lymph courses up the extremity towards the thorax.

3. If the wounds from the teeth have produced lacerations, incision may not be necessary. On the contrary, if the teeth have been disengaged in such a manner that only punctures are present, a short longitudinal incision should be made at each site where a tooth has penetrated. These incisions should be made using the same precautions and techniques as described for making multiple incisions in snakebite first aid treatment (see Part VIII, Section B-2).

4. Suction should then be applied to the lacerations or incisions for the purpose of mechanically removing from the subcutaneous tissue spaces as much of the venom as possible. It is considered advisable to continue local wound suction for at least one-half hour, but a longer period may be desirable in deep bites.

The suction may be applied utilizing any one of the techniques, oral or mechanical, described under snakebite first aid treatment (see Part VIII, Section B-3). Likewise, the same general precautions should be observed.

5. Should the victim feel weak or on the verge of fainting, it is permissible to employ simple stimulants, such as strong coffee or inhalation of aromatic spirits of ammonia.

6. The First Aider should carry the victim to a doctor or hospital as soon as possible, avoiding any exertion en route by the victim.

7. Continuation treatment. If the symptoms of poisoning do not respond satisfactorily to this treatment but continue to develop, additional treatment is imperative. In such rare cases we recommend shift of the tourniquet ahead of the swelling, followed by new incisions and additional suction, as in the standard snakebite procedure (see Part VIII, Section B-3). We recommend this procedure only for those rare cases of Gila Monster bite that develop alarmingly, and we do so on the basis of evidence given in various case descriptions in the literature. It is not a standard procedure, because of the rarity of alarmingly severe Gila Monster bites, but it is evidently a valid procedure in those rare cases.

F. MEDICAL TREATMENT

According to the authorities in this field (e.g., Shannon), the physician's ministrations are directed toward three ends:

1. Shock must be anticipated, and appropriate measures be undertaken to prevent or treat it. It may be necessary to employ the use of oxygen, blood transfusion, antishock or restorative drugs (e.g., metrazol), and other measures.

2. In dealing with the systemic effects of the venom, mainly neurotoxic in nature, the physician's armamentar-

ium is limited. The customary anti-shock drugs are helpful, but there is no specific antivenin for counteracting the effects of lizard venom.

3. The mouths of lizards almost invariably contain pathogenic bacteria. Appropriate antibiotics should be administered to prevent secondary bacterial infections, and tetanus (gas gangrene) antitoxin likewise should be considered.

PART V

VENOMOUS OPHIDIA (Snakes)

A. GENERAL ZOOLOGICAL CHARACTERISTICS OF THE SUBORDER OPHIDIA

Because snakes include most of the species of venomous vertebrates, their anatomical and physiological features shall be discussed in some detail.

1. Size

Snakes vary greatly in size and weight, the largest of them (e.g., Pythons) being in length 30 feet, in thickness 10 inches, and in weight 150 pounds. The ordinary snakes seen in North America are moderate in size (from three to five feet long, and from one to two inches thick), and the average of them weighs from one-half to two pounds. There are very small snakes, too, measuring only a few inches in length, a sixteenth of an inch in thickness, and weighing only a fraction of an ounce.

2. Skeletal System

Snakes are reptiles that have lost their legs, and even most of the bones inside the body to which legs are attached in most other reptiles. The number of vertebrae in the backbone of snakes may number as many as 300 in some species, and there is a correspondingly greater number of ribs. This explains the great elongation of snakes' bodies. There is no sternum, and the ribs are elongated and curved ventrally (towards the front).

3. Locomotion

The internal machinery of ribs, backbone, and muscles is extremely complicated and enables snakes to wriggle and bend in almost any direction. Horizontal undulatory movements are responsible for rapid movement. Sidewinding is characteristic of certain species. At times heavy-bodied species of snakes move in a straight line with the body outstretched gliding in a caterpillar-like fashion by moving the large belly scales back and forth over the ends of the ribs. Movements of the ribs themselves are not involved in any type of locomotion in snakes.

All snakes can swim. Most can remain under water for several hours without drowning, not because they previously inhale large quantities of air, but because the oxygen present in their lungs and tissues suffices for hours of life at the slow rates of metabolism characteristic of reptiles.

The tail varies from nearly one-half to one-eighth of the total length. It is of special aid in locomotion in certain arboreal species through possession of prehensile powers, and in certain aquatic species by being flattened like a fish tail.

Contrary to many folk tales, snakes do NOT move rapidly. Actual measurements have shown that one of the swiftest species, the Blue Racer, never travels over three to four miles an hour. Any adult confronted by a snake, if not frightened to a standstill, can outrun it easily, regardless of its kind.

4. Skin

The covering of snakes is entirely one of scales which are nothing but a hyper-development of the *horny layer* of the skin wherein the cells are converted into keratin (horn). The undersurface scales are so made as to grip earth, branch, or whatever they may be traversing, and thus aid locomotion. In the average species of snake, the "skin" is shed approximately three times a year (season). The "slough" or "moult" is not actually the entire skin, but only the extreme outermost, dead layers of the epidermis that are constantly being formed by steady growth from underneath. It is only the layer of dead cells that is periodically shed. Snakes shed the "moult" as a whole, beginning at the lips and turning it backward and inside out.

Snake skin is essentially "dry," as it possesses few or no dermal glands. Thus it is not correct to regard snakes as "slimy" creatures.

5. Rattles

Rattles (Fig. 3), not present except in certain so-called Pit Vipers, are skin or epidermal appendages at the end of the tail, and are made up of a series of hollow rings of dry keratin. Vibration of the rings, as when the snake is disturbed, produces a rattle-like succession of short sharp noises.

The rings composing a rattle are loosely locked together by a series of alternating ridges and grooves. They become disjointed ordinarily only toward the tip, as a result of long wear. The maximum number of segments a snake may retain in its rattle is dependent largely upon the activity of the snake, and the extent of use of the rattles. Any rattle of more than ten rings is a long one.

Every time the skin of the snake is shed, one more ring is added to the base of the rattle at the end of the tail. The age of a snake cannot accurately be told by the number of segments or rings present because the skin may

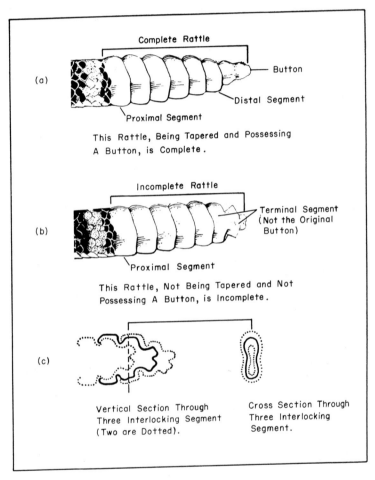

Fig. 3. The rattle of a Rattlesnake.

(a) The intact rattle of a young snake. (Adapted from Klauber.)

(b) An incomplete rattle of an old snake. (Adapted from Klauber.)

(c) Sectional views of the structure of a rattle. (Adapted from Schmidt and Davis.)

be shed two or three times in a single season, and some rings may have been lost. If the small, rounded terminal "button" is still intact (the button which was present when the snake was born), the age can be ascertained approximately by totaling the number of rings and dividing by three.

6. Teeth

Most species of snakes lack venom and possess numerous, relatively small teeth situated in two rows on the palate (roof of mouth) as well as on the jawbones (two upper and two lower; Fig. 4). These small teeth are slender and conical in shape, and are curved backward.

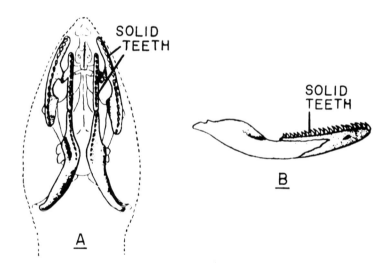

Fig. 4. Tooth pattern in a non-poisonous snake. (Adapted from Pope.)

A. Ventral view of the skull with lower jaws removed; note the four rows of small solid teeth.

B. Lateral view of the right lower jaw, showing single row of numerous small teeth.

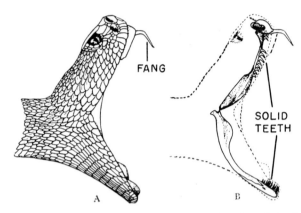

FANG

SOLID
TEETH

A   B

Fig. 5. Lateral view of a head of a snake (rattlesnake) showing
exposed fangs approximately in biting position. (Adapted
from Pope.)
A. Tissues intact as in a live snake.
B. Position of the tooth bearing bones.

All snakes having a venom capable of producing any
marked effect upon human beings, possess some teeth
known as "fangs" which are specialized structures for the
conduction of venom (Fig. 5). Basically fangs are shaped
like the other teeth, being curved and slender, but usually
are at least somewhat larger. The specializations of fangs
enabling them to perform the unique function of conduction of venom are of two sorts. Some fangs are hollow like
hypodermic needles (Fig. 6), whereas others possess a
groove down one side. As shall be described later in this
section, snakes with hollow fangs inject (i.e., squirt) the
poison from the venom sacs into the bitten prey, whereas
in the cases of snakes possessing only grooved fangs, the
venom flows along the grooves into the tissues of the bitten
prey.

Three types or arrangements of fangs occur in snakes:
(a) small, grooved, FIXED fangs, one to 4 in number on

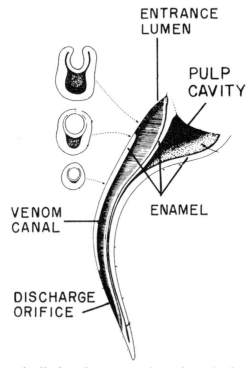

Fig. 6. Longitudinal and cross sections through the fang of a
rattlesnake. (Adapted from Bogert.)

Fig. 7. Right upper jaw of a snake with FIXED rear fangs.
(Adapted from Bogert.)

each side, at the REAR of the upper jaw (Fig. 7); (b) hollow, FIXED fangs, one on each side, at the FRONT of the upper jaw (Fig. 8); and (c) hollow, MOVABLE fangs, one on each side, at the FRONT of the upper jaw

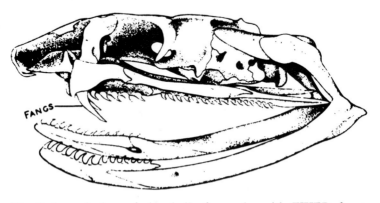

Fig. 8. Lateral view of the skull of a snake with FIXED front fangs. (Adapted from Bogert.)

(Fig. 9). Numerous species of the first type occur all over the world, including the United States, but the venom is not deadly (except in a few African species) and the systemic effects are seldom even as serious as those of a bee sting. Most species having front fangs, on the other hand, and belonging to types *b* and *c* above, are deadly venomous.

All teeth are regularly replaced (Fig. 10) at intervals of perhaps two weeks to a month, and teeth that are accidentally lost are quickly renewed (including fangs, Fig. 10). Hence, a snake from which the fangs have been removed (e.g., as sometimes is done for circuses or carnival sideshows) soon becomes dangerous again.

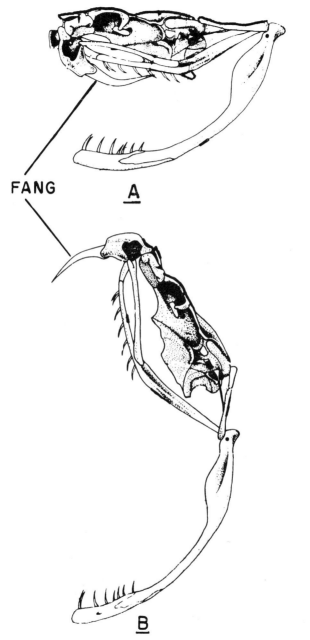

FANG

<u>A</u>

<u>B</u>

Fig. 9. Lateral views of the skull of a snake with MOVABLE
    front fangs. (Adapted from Klauber.)
    A. Mouth closed, showing fang retracted.
    B. Mouth open, showing fang protracted.

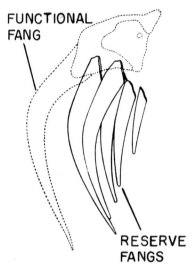

FUNCTIONAL
FANG

RESERVE
FANGS

Fig. 10. The functional and reserve fangs of a rattlesnake as
seen in lateral view. (Adapted from Klauber.)

7. Ears

Snakes have no auditory openings, no middle ear
cavities, and do not detect their enemies by air-borne
sounds. For this reason, for example, a Rattlesnake cannot
hear its own rattle. All snakes perceive ground-borne
sounds, however; the inner ear, which is the actual sound
receptor, is well developed. Snakes are deaf only to air-
borne sounds.

8. Eyes

Snakes have eyes (Fig. 11), and can see. They are
more sensitive to movement than to form. There are no
moveable eyelids, but instead the lids are fused together
in a permanently closed position, and are perfectly trans-
parent. When the skin covering is shed, the eye covering

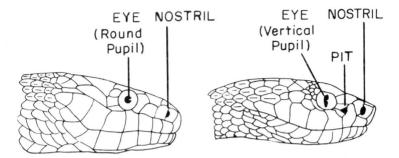

Fig. 11. Lateral view of the head of a harmless snake (A), and of a pit viper (B). (Adapted from Blanchard.)

also is shed. Snakes' eyes are always "open," but, for a few days shortly before the periodic shedding of the skin slough, the eyes are "milky" (as is all the rest of the skin, but the skin discoloration is not so easily seen), and the snakes see poorly at this time.

The pupils of snakes' eyes may be vertical or round, and they expand and contract in response to the intensity of the light just as happens in the case of humans' eyes.

9. Tongue

This structure is long, slender, and forked at the end. It is NOT a poisonous structure, anatomically or physiologically, but rather serves as an aid for detecting odors in the air. By this means the snake can detect nearby or approaching prey, friend or enemy. Snakes are reluctant to move about when preparing to moult, not only because the eyes are "milky" and they cannot see well, but also because they cannot smell well. The covering at the forked tips of the tongue is shed at about the same time as the skin, and while preparing to molt its cover, the tongue cannot operate efficiently as an olfactory accessory.

10. Pits

Some venomous snakes, the Pit Vipers, possess a peculiar depression, a *facial pit* (Fig. 11), located between the nostrils and the eyes. These pits are thermoreceptive structures which are very sensitive to temperature changes in the external environment. The pits are particularly useful to snakes in detecting warm-blooded animals where they cannot be seen, as for example at night or in holes in trees, among rocks or underground.

In illustration, when a Pit Viper puts its head a short distance into a ground hole, it can very shortly learn without further exploration whether or not there is a warm-blooded animal anywhere in the underground passages connected with the hole. The heat radiated by the warm-blooded animal therein is registered or detected by the snakes' pit organ, even though the difference in temperature at the distance of several feet is but a small fraction of a degree. Since most Pit Vipers (curiously enough, not Cottonmouths, and sometimes not Copperheads) feed exclusively upon warm-blooded animals, the pit organ is an extremely useful device for finding prey.

11. Body Temperature

Like other reptiles, snakes are "cold-blooded" in the sense that they are incapable of controlling their own body temperature except by moving from one place to another.

12. Respiration

Both young and adult snakes breathe only with lungs.

13. Bladder

Snakes possess no urinary bladder. Wastes from the kidneys are excreted as a white, solid uric acid material through the *cloaca*, a chamber opening on the under surface of the body at the base of the tail. The cloaca also serves as the outlet for fecal matter released by the alimentary tract.

14. Copulation and Breeding

Snakes possess a pair of generative organs located in the base of the tail. During copulation only one of the organs is used at a time despite the fact that two are present. Males court females in an astonishingly gentle fashion, and copulating snakes do not display the brutal element so often evident in other animals during the mating process. Even combat between male snakes (over the possession of a territory or of a female snake) is a sort of "Indian wrestling"; fighting snakes do not bite each other under natural conditions unless the intent of one is to eat the other.

Most snakes lay eggs in the ground, in logs or under ground surface cover. They give the eggs no care after they are laid. A few snakes bring their young forth alive.

15. Diet

Snakes all live on other animals (e.g., frogs, other and smaller snakes, birds, worms, insects, fish, etc.), or on their eggs. They often swallow dead animals (carrion).

During winter hibernation snakes do not eat; they subsist upon fat stored in their bodies and obtained from food consumed before going into hibernation. This suffices since their bodily metabolism during hibernation is extremely low. When snakes are out and active, as between early spring and late fall months, they usually eat no oftener than once or twice a week.

16. Catching Their Prey

Snakes handle their food in several ways: (a) They may take the object (prey) in their mouths and swallow it whole, either dead or alive. Examples of snakes doing this are Garter Snakes, Water Snakes and Blue Racers (Black Snakes). Prey that offers resistance may be subdued by holding it down with loops of the body and by lacerating the victim with the teeth. (b) Or, they may catch the animal they intend to eat, squeeze it to death in their coils, and then swallow it whole but dead. Examples of snakes using this "constrictor" technique are Bull Snakes, King Snakes, Boa Constrictors, Pythons. (c) Or, they may bite their prey and poison it by injecting venom into the victim, and then swallow it after it is dead. Examples of snakes utilizing this technique are Rattlesnakes, Copperheads, Water Moccasins, Coral Snakes, Fer-de-lance Snakes, Sea Snakes, and Cobras. Sometimes the prey is released when struck by a venomous snake; at other times it is held in the mouth, depending upon the size and vigor of resistance of the prey.

17. Deglutition (Swallowing Mechanism)

Snakes do NOT chew their food, but must swallow it whole, or not at all. Animals several times as thick as the snake can be swallowed because the bones in the jaws are loosely connected with elastic ligaments.

When a snake swallows food, the backward-curved teeth on the jaws on one side hold the object while those on the jaw on the other side are thrust forward into a new hold. By this means of alternately advancing the teeth on one side and then on the other, the food is gradually forced down the throat into the esophagus and stomach. Thus, a

small Garter Snake can swallow a large frog, and a large
Python can swallow a small calf.

18. Erroneous Beliefs About Snakes

a. *Hypnotism.* Contrary to many folk tales, snakes do
NOT fascinate or hypnotize people or other animals.
However, humans and other animals suddenly confronted
by a snake may be frightened to a standstill and appear to
be hypnotized.

b. *Licking Their Prey.* Snakes do NOT lick their prey
in order to cover the victim animal with slime to make
swallowing easier. They do "smell" it carefully with the
tongue before eating it, presumably to verify that it is
dead and to detect the head, which is usually swallowed
first.

c. *The Joint Snake.* This folk tale tells of a curious
snake that flies into pieces (like shattered glass) when
struck with a stick. The pieces are said to re-unite, and
the reconstructed snake crawls away if one leaves it un-
disturbed. But, this myth is also false.

This extraordinary story has some basis. The so-called
"Joint Snake" is NOT a snake, but rather is a species of
lizard. Most lizards are able to lose their tails without serious injury and with the benefit that they are likely to escape unnoticed while their enemies are dealing with the
wriggling tail. In many lizards, among them the so-called
"Joint Snake," this capacity to lose the tail is highly developed. The tail breaks at any of many special breakage
planes, and the muscle bundles are so arranged that they
contract and close the severed arteries thus preventing the
loss of blood. It is NOT true that the pieces will join together again, but it is some compensation for the lizard

that it is able to grow a perfectly satisfactory new tail. The body is never voluntarily broken—only the tail.

d. *The Blow Snake*. Throughout eastern North America a snake is found bearing a most evil reputation for its purported ability to blow its venom a considerable distance into the victim's face, sometimes causing a temporary blindness, and sometimes convulsions. This is another erroneous legend.

The fact is that the Blow Snake (occasionally referred to as the Puff Adder) possesses an unusually large, broad head. When the snake confronts an intruder, it flattens and broadens both the head and forepart of the body, meantime swaying the body, and hissing loudly as it exhales rapidly through the partly opened mouth. This suggests the idea to the observer that the snake is ready to blow venom into the victim's face. This puffing mechanism actually represents a form of bluff, for the snakes not only completely lack venom, but could not blow it if they had it. In fact, despite the frightening bluff, these snakes can scarcely be made to bite anything except their food animals. They dart the head toward their annoyers as though ready to bite, but they do not open the mouth far enough to bite.

e. *The Hoop Snake*. Another false myth peculiar to North America pertains to the so-called Hoop Snake. This creature, according to folk tale, is able to progress over the ground by taking its tail in its mouth, and rolling like a hoop. The snake is believed to be capable of launching itself like a javelin at an enemy.

The truth is that there is no acceptable scientific record of any snake having the capacity to grab its tail in its mouth, and roll over the ground like a hoop. This is pure fiction, and is based on illusionary observations.

f. *The Milk Snake.* Another erroneous legend about snakes is that some particular species suck milk from cows. The ability of any snake to fasten itself to a cow's udder and suck milk must be considered a plain impossibility. If the rows of needle-like teeth in a snake's mouth were applied to a cow's sensitive teat, the cow would be driven into a frenzy, and the snake would be dislodged by being stepped upon or kicked. Experiment proves that snakes dislike milk, will not voluntarily drink it, and are actually made ill when forced to swallow it.

A possible source of this fable is the fact that some of the egg-laying snakes frequent barnyards for the purpose of laying their eggs in manure or compost piles. Most farmers, when they kill a culprit snake in their barnyards, do so with such fury that little if any is left intact. The crushed eggs of a gravid (pregnant) snake would give forth a milk-like fluid, and this might be observed as confirmatory evidence for the belief in their ability to suck cows.

g. *Mother Snake Swallowing Young.* Contrary to this false myth, snakes do NOT swallow their young to protect them from imminent danger. This folk tale has arisen because of reports of female (mother) snakes being found with tails of snakes in their mouths which wriggle around until they disappear down the snake's throat.

This optical illusion is best explained by the following observations regarding snakes' habits. Some common snakes are known to feed on other snakes and on some small lizards (which may resemble closely a snake), and the tails of such prey could be seen to wriggle as they disappear down the snake's throat. Furthermore, snakes are commonly killed by humans with brutal violence, and it is quite possible that a pregnant mother snake bearing live snakes might easily be thought to contain the snakes in the stomach rather than the uterus.

h. *Snakes with Tail Stingers.* Another erroneous folk tale about snakes is that some species, usually the so-called Hoop Snakes, possess in their tail a venomous "stinger." These creatures often are referred to as Stinging Snakes because of the belief that they strike their prey with the "stinger" and thereby poison them.

This legend appears to be based on the behavior of certain snakes which, when held in the hand or even when confined with a stick, make exploring or apparently pricking movements with the tip of the tail. When, in addition, the tail ends have a sharp horny spine, some excuse is afforded for the belief in a tail sting. No reptiles of any sort anywhere in the world possess any poison whatever in the tail.

i. *Crushing Their Prey.* It is often said or thought that the constrictor snakes, such as our native Bull Snakes and Rat Snakes, and the exotic Boas and Pythons, crush the body in relentlessly tightening coils that break every bone of the body. Such is not the case. All constrictors squeeze only hard enough to prevent movement; a struggling prey causes the snake to tighten its coils; a completely quiet animal receives little pressure. At most, the strength of a snake is seldom capable of breaking any bones of its prey; it is used simply to suffocate the animal by preventing the movements necessary for breathing.

j. *Horsehair Ropes.* There is a popular belief that horsehair ropes (as opposed to manila or other ropes) will not be crossed by a snake, and that such a rope laid out on the ground or floor around a cot or bedroll will keep snakes away. There is no truth whatsoever in this belief. Snakes of all kinds cross horsehair ropes without hesitation. Neither this nor any other object or substance now known can serve as a specific snake repellant whether utilized in this or in any other way.

k. *Snakes Biting Under Water.* According to a rather widespread belief, snakes cannot bite under water, at least not effectively. Repeated observations by students of the ways of snakes have conclusively shown, however, that any snake can bite under water and that many kinds frequently do so. Stepping on a venomous snake under water is just as potentially dangerous as doing so on land.

B. VENOMOUS SNAKES IN THE UNITED STATES

1. Kinds of Venomous Snakes

In the United States *two* main types of deadly venomous snakes are considered to exist.

a. *Coral Snakes.* Of these there are two genera, and two species. As shall be described in detail in Part VII, Coral Snakes are recognized by a peculiar color pattern (red, black, and yellow bands), by possessing FIXED FRONT fangs, absence of pits, and absence of rattles.

There are several species of harmless snakes whose appearance "mimics" that of Coral Snakes. But, close scrutiny permits their differentiation from true Coral Snakes.

b. *Pit Vipers.* Of these there is one family, but several (17) species. As shall be described in detail in Part VII, Pit Vipers are recognized by the following anatomical observations (Fig. 12): they possess MOVEABLE FRONT fangs; pits are present on their heads, located between the nostrils and eyes; many Pit Vipers, but not all, possess rattles.

Their skin color patterns are distinctive enough to be recognized by expert herpetologists, but not by most First Aiders.

Fig. 12. A prairie rattlesnake. (Adapted from Hallowell.)

Pit Vipers can be classified into two main groups, (a) RATTLESNAKES, of which there are two genera, and 15 species. (b) MOCCASINS, of which there are one genus, and two species—Copperheads and Cottonmouths.

* *Summary.* The statement is often made that there are four kinds of venomous snakes in the United States (*i.e.*, Coral Snakes, Rattlesnakes, Cottonmouths, and Copperheads). But, this is NOT correct. Actually, the number of groupings depends on the level of classification desired. The four groups mentioned above cut across several levels of classification. Any of the following groupings of venomous snakes in the United States may be accepted as correct according to modern zoological taxonomy:

—On the basis of *families*, TWO groups (*Elapidae* for Coral Snakes, and *Crotalidae* for others).

—On the basis of *subfamilies*, THREE groups (Coral Snakes, Rattlesnakes, and Moccasins).

—On the basis of *genera*, FIVE groups (two of Coral Snakes, two of Rattlesnakes, and one of Moccasins).

—On the basis of *species*, NINETEEN groups (two of Coral Snakes, 15 of Rattlesnakes, and two of Moccasins).

2. Proportion of Deadly to Non-Deadly Snakes in the United States

a. According to the relative number of *specimens* estimated to exist, perhaps three per cent of snakes found in the United States are venomous.

b. According to the relative number of *species* in the United States, 10 per cent of snakes are venomous. This is a relatively low figure. In Australia, at the other extreme, the figure is perhaps 70 per cent.

c. Considering the number of *families* of snakes that exist, five in a total of 13 families contain venomous species.

—PIT VIPERS, *Crotalidae* (mostly New World). Outstanding characteristics are FRONT MOVE-ABLE fangs, and pits.

—TRUE VIPERS, *Viperidae* (exclusively Old World). Characterized chiefly by FRONT MOVEABLE fangs, and NO pits.

—CORALLINE SNAKES, *Elapidae* (all Old World except Coral Snakes which are found from southern United States to South America). These have FRONT FIXED fangs, and are not marine (aquatic).

—SEA SNAKES, *Hydrophiidae* (only found in Pacific and Indian ocean regions). Notable for having FRONT FIXED fangs, and being marine.

—COMMON SNAKE FAMILY, *C o l u b r i d a e* (worldwide except in the seas and in cold regions). Seventy per cent of all species of snakes belong to this family. Most of them are non-poisonous, the bite (excluding secondary infections and lacera-tions) being totally innocuous. Only perhaps 15 per cent possess venom, and of these only a few African species are deadly venomous. The bite of other venomous species of this family produces a reaction of no greater severity in human beings than an ordinary bee-sting. The common snake family is characterized by having FIXED REAR fangs, if fangs are present at all. Fangs are ABSENT in the non-venomous species, PRESENT in the venomous ones.

3. Mode of Envenomation

All venomous snakes possess *fangs* (for detailed description, see Part V, Sect. A-6) which are notable for being either hollow or grooved, and they also possess venom sacs. The fangs and venom sacs are connected by a duct. The venom sacs are supplied by, and lie against, two modified salivary glands which secrete the poison. These modified salivary glands and the venom sacs are found on both sides of the head, and are situated just behind the eyes (Fig. 13). The sacs are capable of distention and can be contracted.

When a venomous snake bites a victim, the full or distended venom sacs are compressed simultaneously with the

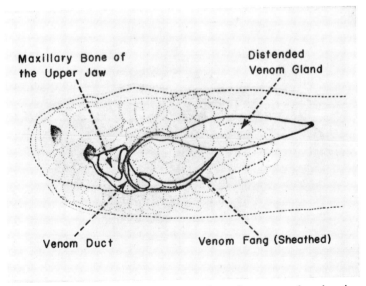

Fig. 13. Phantom view of the head of a poisonous snake, showing the venom apparatus. (Adapted from Klauber.)

closing of the jaws, and the venom is released into the victim's subcutaneous tissues. In venomous snakes with hollow fangs, the venom is ejected through the fang into the victim's tissues in a manner similar to that of expressing fluid out of a hypodermic syringe through the needle. In venomous snakes with grooves on the surfaces of the fangs, the venom is expressed from the venom ducts into the groove on the fangs, and then flows through the grooves during the biting process into the victim's tissues.

In the United States, all venomous snakes envenomate by biting or striking the victim as described just above. In a few African Cobras, envenomation is by "spitting" (actually squirting, for snakes cannot spit) the venom through the fangs into the victim's eyes.

The Coral Snakes (and all other snakes with FIXED FRONT fangs) have relatively short fangs, and thus tend to chew in the process of envenomation, imbedding the fangs deeply, and assuring penetration of venom into the tissues of the prey. On the contrary, the Vipers have long fangs which do not need to be forced by chewing to reach into the deeper tissues of the prey; such snakes usually stab quickly, with but a momentary bite, and then release themselves.

4. Mode of Spread of Venom

There are two possible avenues for spread of venom received from the bite or strike of a snake:

a. *By the Direct Blood Circulation.* Very rarely does the bite of a venomous snake cause injection of the venom directly into a large blood vessel. When it does happen the venom spreads rapidly throughout the victim's body, and death often occurs within a few minutes.

b. *By the Lymphatic Circulation.* This is the usual mode of spread of venom in cases of snake bite. The venom or-

dinarily is received by the victim in the lymphatic (interstitial) spaces of muscle or subcutaneous tissues. The venom
travels with the lymph, slowly spreading as the lymph
flows. The lymphatic channels of significance in snake
bite cases are located mainly in the loose subcutaneous
tissues. Much of the lymph with its venom can readily be
drained from these areas by proper application of known
first aid techniques.

When a snake bites a person, the venom leaves the tips
of the hollow or grooved fangs imbedded in the soft subcutaneous tissues, and instantaneously spreads several mil-
limeters in all directions. Certain fractions of the venom
destroy by chemical digestion all tissues with which it
comes in contact, and in particular destroys small blood
vessels as it goes, releasing blood cells and lymph among
the injured tissue cells. The venom moves slowly with the
lymph, unless the muscles are active. Eventually, if the
venom is not mostly removed by suction from the subcutaneous tissue spaces by the technique to be described
later on in Part VIII, it enters the veins and general circulation in the region of the upper thorax, and thence is
carried by the blood stream to all parts of the body. As the
venom passes through the liver it undergoes detoxification.
If the liver is overwhelmed by venom little significant detoxification can occur, and the victim likely will die. However, if the first aid suction technique has been promptly
and effectively carried out, relatively little venom will
gain access to the blood stream. What does get into it can
be detoxified, and the victim has a high probability of
survival.

5. Composition of Snake Venoms

Snake venom when dry appears as yellow crystals. The
venom is a highly complex protein mixture, enzymatic in

action, and contains at least eleven different physiological fractions, listed as follows:

a. *Coagulant.* Causes abnormal blood coagulation.

b. *Anti-Coagulant.* Causes abnormal deficiency in blood coagulation. This fraction thus promotes "internal bleeding."

c. *Agglutinin.* Causes the production of abnormal agglutination (clumping) of red blood cells. When this fraction predominates, blood flow in the small vessels is obstructed, and the tissues tend to become oxygen-deficient because the agglutinated cells cannot yield as much oxygen as separate cells. Sluggish clumps of cells such as these cannot flow normally in and out of the microscopic tissue capillaries. Thus they cannot deliver the normal oxygen supply to the tissues and organs, and they augment tissue swelling through impairment of circulatory drainage.

d. *Anti-Bactericidin.* When this fraction predominates, the blood loses its ability to fight bacteria. The wounds in the body become rapidly and severely infected, the body defense against such infection is lost, and the victim can die of uncontrolled suppuration.

e. *Neurotoxin-A.* This fraction affects the central nervous system, especially the cardio-respiratory brain centers. When this occurs the victim dies promptly of paralysis (chiefly respiratory, as in fatal polio cases).

f. *Neurotoxin-B.* In action this fraction affects primarily skeletal muscles, resulting in general muscular paralysis. Death can occur when the thoracic wall respiratory muscles are so affected, even when the respiratory center in the brain stem may be unaffected.

g. *Cytolysins.* Cause death of all cells in contact with the venom, by destruction of the cell walls.

h. *Proteolysins.* Cause destruction (by lysis) of all tissue proteins.

i. *Cardiac Stimulator.* This fraction (Cardiotoxin of Ghosh and Sarkar, 1956: 190) causes abnormal speeding of the heart and circulation rates by virtue of its stimulatory effect on the heart muscle fibers. Thus a heart so affected literally "races" itself to exhaustion, and death follows.

j. *Autotoxins.* These are enzymes or other compounds that cause certain organs, such as the liver, to produce abnormally pathological substances independently causing damage to the body.

k. *Spreading Factors.* Reference is made here to some biochemical factors, including hyaluronidase among other substances, which effect a rapid dispersal of the venom through the tissues.

l. *Cholinesterase.* Most snake venoms contain a substance, an enzyme called cholinesterase, which breaks down the chemical acetylcholine which is essential for conduction of nervous impulses between cells of the nervous system, and between their terminal fibers and the muscle or gland cells (at the myoneural junction) they supply. A paralytic effect results.

m. *Anti-Cholinesterase.* At least some snakes possess an anti-cholinesterase in addition to cholinesterase (Lee, Chang and Kamijo, 1956: 197).

n. *Phosphatases.* These are enzymes that destroy adenosine triphosphate, a substance essential for contraction of muscles. A paralytic effect results.

o. *Inhibitors of Respiratory Enzymes.* The enzymes that are essential for cellular respiration—that is, for release of energy by breaking down sugar molecules—are destroyed by certain principles of snake venoms (Ghosh and Sarkar, 1956: 193). Tissues thus affected die if respiration cannot be restored within about 5 minutes.

6. Over-all Actions of Venoms

When a person is a victim of a venomous snake, the physiological-pathological bodily responses fall into one of the following two patterns: the *neurotoxic response,* and the *hemopathic response.*

A neurotoxic response is one that involves any sort of chemical impairment of the normal function of any part of the nervous system, or of the neuro-muscular junctions. A *hemopathic response* is one that involves any sort of direct chemical impairment of the normal function of any part of the circulatory system, including both the blood vessels and the blood itself. The total hemopathic effects of snake venoms have been referred to by many authors as the *hemotoxic* response, and by other authors as the *hemorrhagic* response. Neither of the latter terms properly embraces the total hemopathic effect, however, although each is quite appropriate in reference to certain aspects of the total effect. Properly defined, as agreed by all medical and standard dictionaries consulted, a hemotoxic response is one that involves chemical impairment of the normal function of any part of the blood, including especially blood cells. Destruction, clumping and other abnormal alterations of the red blood cells are often important aspects of the hemotoxic response. Conversely, a hemorrhagic response, properly defined, is one that involves destruction or fracture of the *endothelium,* the very thin inner lining of arteries and veins. The endothelium also forms the entire wall of the capillaries, those minute microscopic blood vessels connecting the smallest ramifications of the arteries with those of the veins. The result of destruction of the endothelium is a hemorrhage (escape of blood from its vessels) into adjacent tissues or areas. Hemorrhagins also destroy the walls of lymphatic vessels, and in fact are more important in snake venom for this action than for damage to blood vessels, although both phenomena occur.

The hemopathogens of snake venom, therefore, include both hemotoxins, affecting blood and/or blood cells thereof, and hemorrhagins, affecting blood and lymph vessels. It is confusing to refer to the *total* hemopathic effect of snake venoms as either "hemotoxic" or "hemorrhagic", for the effect is both (with rare if any exception). Accordingly we here propose that the much more appropriate and more general term "hemopathic" be utilized for reference to the total effects of snake venom upon the blood *and* blood vascular system, and that the terms "hemotoxic" and "hemorrhagic" continue to be used in their properly narrow, medical sense.

In proposing the use of the term "hemopathic" in this sense, we are assured that "hemo" in Greek applies equally well either to the blood itself or to the blood vascular system, and that "pathos" in Greek refers broadly to any "suffering" condition. "Hemopathic" has been applied previously to diseased conditions of the blood, yet this word is so perfectly adapted by its philology to use for the total direct circulatory effects of snake venom (excluding those effects of neurotoxic origin) that we recommend enlargement of its English usage to embrace this meaning, rather than coinage of a new term which could scarcely be equally appropriate.

Before discussing these two over-all responses, it is important to emphasize that the venom of almost all snakes produces a combination of neurotoxic and hemopathic changes, the exact relative importance or incidence of the two responses varying according to the species of snake.

Few species have a purely neurotoxic or purely hemo-pathic venom. Treatment, as shall be considered in Parts VIII and IX, varies primarily with the preponderance of neurotoxins versus hemopathogens.

a. Neurotoxic Response

In venomous snake bite cases occurring in the United States, the neurotoxic response (i.e., affecting the nervous system) is seen most clearly in Coral Snake cases. The neurotoxic response is also seen to a lesser extent in poisoning by Pit Vipers, varying in accordance with the species, because the venom of some of the Pit Vipers usually does contain some neurotoxic fractions.

When a victim receives venom that is chiefly neuro-toxic in action, the *chief signs and symptoms* that develop are as follows:

—*Circulatory Impairment.* Cardiac arrhythmia or paralysis (partial or complete), resulting in depression of heart output, decrease in blood pressure, generalized weakness, exhaustion, etc., terminating in shock. These symptoms and signs result from action of the venom upon the nerves of the heart.

—*Headache.* Severe headaches may follow upon peripheral vascular changes of neurotoxic origin.

—*Vertigo.* Physical giddiness, unsteadiness, and dizziness are the usual manifestations when venom acts upon the proprioceptors of the inner ear or the nerves pertaining thereto.

—*Loss or impairment of sight.* Caused by action of the venom upon the retina or optic nerve and tract.

—*Auditory disturbance.* Complaints involving hearing have been reported in some cases, and are to be expected in association with action of the venom upon the inner ear or auditory centers or nerves.

—*Mental disturbance.* Incoherent speech, mental confusion, stupor, or unconsciousness are the usual manifestations of mental disturbance when the gray matter of the brain is affected by the venom.

—*Locomotor disturbance.* Caused by neurotoxin-B (see 5-f above).

—*Muscular spasms or twitching.* Effects of the venom upon the pyramidal or motor tracts of the brain and spinal cord may result in spasmodic activity of the muscles supplied by them.

—*Impaired swallowing.* Caused by neurotoxin-B (see 5-f above).

—*Disturbance of respiration.* Labored or irregular breathing, and shortness of breath (dyspnea) are the usual manifestations. Caused either by neurotoxin-A, or by neurotoxin-B (see 5-e and 5-f above).

—*Cutaneous complaints.* Tingling, numbness (especially about the lips, soles of feet), itching, excessive perspiration and salivation (drooling) are the usual complaints when the venom affects the nerves supplying the skin.

—*Temperature abnormalities.* Fever and/or chills, following upon disturbance of the Temperature Regulating Center in the brain.

—*Gastro-intestinal complaints.* Nausea, vomiting, and diarrhea are the common signs and symptoms resulting from action of the venom upon the nerves to either the muscular or secretory layers of the gut.

It should be emphasized here that neurotoxic venoms do not necessarily effect all of the above symptoms or signs simultaneously. Sometimes only one or two are primarily involved, but it is possible for more or all of them to be present at the same time, especially in fatal cases.

b. Hemopathic Response

The venom of Pit Vipers is mainly hemopathic in nature. The response to the hemopathogens most conspicuously results in tissue swelling occurring at the site of the bite, then spreading to adjacent parts. The cause is mainly the break-down of functional capacity of the lymphatic channels, and the resultant accumulation of undrained lymph in the interstitial spaces between the cells. The swelling itself is excruciatingly painful, and may become so severe as to burst the skin.

A second hemopathic response is the extravasation of blood, escaping from capillaries whose walls are broken down by cytolytic action of the venom. In the general bite area, a bruise-like ecchymosis or discoloration results, but ordinarily no large quantities of blood escape from the vessels. This response may result in the occurrence of throbbing discomfort wherever swelling occurs.

A third hemopathic response, and one of more subtle nature but of no less danger, is destruction of blood cells (all types, not only red blood cells) as well as other tissue cells. The result is that extensive pathological changes occur due to acute tissue anoxia (acute oxygen deficiency) which is caused by the inability of the red blood cells to deliver normal quantities of oxygen.

A fourth hemopathic response also occurs, namely, bleeding from some of the major internal organs into the excretory and alimentary tracts, or into the great visceral spaces. Reference is made to bleeding from the urinary tract accompanying kidney hemorrhage, bleeding from the rectum secondary to intestinal hemorrhage, bleeding into the peritoneal cavity accompanying oozing of blood from the mesenteric vascular bed in the abdomen, and bleeding into the pleural spaces accompanying hemorrhage in the thoracic (chest) wall. Visible and readily recognizable signs and symptoms of this response are appearance of blood in the urine and/or stools, bleeding from the lips, gums, nails and at the site of the bite. Severe headaches may follow upon peripheral vascular changes of hemopathic orgin. Usually thirst also occurs, and may be attributed to decrease in blood volume through losses to extra-vascular areas as described above.

*   *   *   *   *

These are the characteristic responses to neurotoxic and hemopathic poisoning. The venom of almost all snakes produces a combination of these responses, the exact relative importance of the two responses varying according to the species involved in the individual case. It should be emphasized that few species have a purely neurotoxic or purely hemopathic venom. The combination of both types of principles can thus be expected to result, as it does, in the appearance of highly variable combinations of signs and symptoms of both neurotoxic and hemopathic origin.

Putting together these various symptoms and signs of both neurotoxic and hemopathic poisoning, since they often are present in bites by North American Pit Vipers, it is evident that a severe snake bite is one of the most dreadful experiences known to man. Death is horrible, being due eventually to irreversible circulatory failure (cardiac failure, depression of blood pressure, destruction

of red blood cells, loss of blood, extreme shock, etc.), or
to irreversible respiratory failure (terminally seen as paralysis of respiration of central or peripheral nervous system origin).

7. Potency of the Venomous Bite

   a. *Variables Affecting Potency of Bite.*

—SPECIES OF THE OFFENDING SNAKE. Toxicity of
the venom, differing according to species.

—SPECIES OF THE PREY. Resistance of the victim,
natural or acquired.

—CONDITION OF THE SNAKE. The healthier and more
vigorous the snake, the more likely is its venom to
be toxic, and its biting the more sure and certain.

—CONDITION OF THE VICTIM. The healthier and
more vigorous the victim, the greater its resistance
is likely to be.

—SIZE OF THE SNAKE. Generally speaking, the larger
the snake, the greater will be the quantity of venom
injected into the victim at the time of the bite.
However, venomous snakes are dangerous from
birth (or hatching); do not dismiss the bite of a
small snake as of little consequence.

—SENSITIVITY OF THE VICTIM. The sensitivity of
individuals to protein poisons varies considerably in
accordance with previous exposure to those poisons,
and in accordance with genetic make-up.

—SIZE OF THE PREY. The larger the victim, generally
speaking, the longer is the time required for the
venom to pass along the lymphatic channels before
reaching the general blood circulation, and the

greater is the volume of tissue that can serve as a
buffer between the body and the venom. Thus
the larger the size of the victim the greater are the
chances for recovery.

—SITE OF THE BITE. If the bite enters a subcutaneous
artery or vein, rapid death will most likely ensue.
Bites on the face, neck, or trunk usually cannot be
treated as effectively as bites can on the extremities.
Venom received in fatty tissue will be absorbed
more slowly than from other soft tissues.

—EFFECTIVENESS OF THE BITE. Repeated bites by
the offending snake can only result in more serious
poisoning of the victim, rendering recovery less
likely. On the other hand, the snake may strike but
a glancing blow, or may lack fangs or have broken
fangs on one or both sides of its mouth (lost
through accident). It may not imbed the fangs
fully (because of presence of clothing, etc.), or
may not hold on as long as usual, thus greatly
increasing the chances of recovery.

—QUANTITY OF VENOM AVAILABLE. Immediately
after emergence from hibernation, snakes possess
large quantities of venom; the lethal capacity is
thereby greatly increased at such times. On the
contrary, if a victim is bitten but a short time after
the snake has used its venom apparatus, as for
example to kill its prey, the chances of recovery are
augmented.

—VOLUNTARY RESPONSE OF THE VICTIM. The response of the bitten person is of utmost significance
to the outcome. Complete cessation of all voluntary
activity (to be discussed in detail in Part VIII) will
permit the survival of a person, other factors being

equal, who has received several times the amount of venom proving fatal to another victim who succumbs to the temptation of uncontrolled bodily activity.

—Psychological State of Victim. Predisposition of the victim toward hypertension, excitability, nervousness or fearfulness is a severe handicap to rapid recovery from snakebite, for these characteristics promote metabolic activity and more rapid absorption of the venom.

—Psychological State of the Snake. The extent of annoyance (anger or fear) of the snake at the time of the biting has a strongly significant influence upon the amount of venom injected. The snake has complete control upon the amount of venom released at any given time; it can bite without releasing any venom whatever, or with almost complete evacuation of the venom sacs.

b. *Lethal Doses in Snakebites.* These are expressed in *approximate maxima.* By this we mean the maximum number of persons of average weight (154 pounds) that could be killed by the maximum amount of venom known to be expelled in a bite by the cited species.

The following figures represent estimates at maxima for our own species and for some of the world's most venomous species:

TIGER SNAKES (Australian) 20
MAMBA SNAKES (African) 15
COBRAS (Asia & Africa) 15
FER-DE-LANCE SNAKES (So. America) . 10
RATTLESNAKES 10
COTTONMOUTH SNAKES 3
COPPERHEAD SNAKES 2
PIGMY RATTLESNAKES 2
CORAL SNAKES 2

Swaroop and Grab (1956) summarize the deadly ophidian species of each continent, and the number of deaths from snake bite. Apparently the highest percentage of deaths per unit number of bites, in species causing many bites, is held by the krait of India, 77 per cent of bites from which are fatal (Ahuja and Singh, 1956).

In species of American crotalid snakes tested by Gingrich and Hohenadel (1956: 382), the Copperhead rated the lowest value (7-8) in lethal potential for United States species (Pigmy Rattlesnakes were not tested). The Texas Diamond-backed Rattlesnake rated about the same as most other Rattlesnakes—value 10-18—whereas the Cottonmouth had a rated value of 16. The highest ratings for United States snakes were 32-37 in the Florida Diamond-backed Rattlesnake, and 34-52 in various forms of the Prairie Rattlesnake. Various forms of the dreaded tropical American Fer-de-lance (*Bothrops*) rated as high as 55, and the most potent of all in the Americas was found to be the South American Rattlesnake with a rating of 440-480.

c. *Prognosis If Bitten.* About 1500 cases of snake bite occur in the United States every year, and of this number only about 45 result in death. This is only about one tenth of one per cent of the number of fatalities from automobile accidents that occur per year in this country. The low rate of snake-bite mortality may seem incredible in view of the tremendous lethal potential of snakebite (see the preceding paragraph 7-b), but in reality almost never is the maximal lethal potential closely approximated in any given case (see the list of variables in the preceding paragraph 7-a).

COMMON RATTLESNAKES. Those persons bitten by non-pigmy (common) Rattlesnakes have from zero to

20 (average about 19) out of 20 chances for recovery if standard first aid treatment measures are promptly and efficiently carried out, and followed subsequently by proper medical care. Without proper treatment (first aid, and medical), the chances of recovery still vary from zero to 20 out of 20 chances, but the average approaches 5 in 20, or even less. The bites vary so greatly in dangerousness that an average figure for recovery, either with or without treatment, is likely to be misleading as a guide to expected outcome in any given case. Each case must be considered individually as it develops, not as an "average" case until events so prove it. A Rattlesnake bite is always a deadly serious matter, and recovery hinges very importantly upon the efficiency of the first aid treatment instituted.

Fifteen per cent of the bites from the Florida Diamond-backed Rattlesnake, for example, have resulted in death in recent years, even with improved techniques of treatment. This is the most dangerous snake in the United States (as well as the largest, on the basis of weight, of all venomous snakes in the world), yet the Western Diamond-backed Rattlesnake causes more deaths from snakebite than any other species in the country, simply because of the greater frequency of bites inflicted by that species.

MOCCASINS AND PIGMY RATTLESNAKES. The chances for recovery from bites of these snakes, if properly treated, average perhaps 24 in 25 (96 per cent). Without treatment, the chances for recovery average perhaps five in ten (50 per cent). In fact, less than a half-dozen deaths from the bites of Pigmy Rattlesnakes and Copperheads, out of many hundreds that have occurred, have ever been recorded to have terminated fatally. These are the least dangerous of the venomous snakes, but deaths have been recorded from the bites of each kind. Actually there are two species of Pigmy Rattlesnakes, a southern and a northern. The southern species is the only species of venomous snake in this country that has never been recorded to have caused a human death, although it undoubtedly could kill small children or weakened adults.

CORAL SNAKES. In the absence of prompt and adequate treatment, which cannot always be given because of the speed with which Coral Snake poisoning develops, death is probable in perhaps 50 per cent of cases. With proper and prompt treatment, an average of perhaps 95 per cent of cases should recover. In actuality perhaps 10 to 15 per cent of Coral Snake bites have resulted in death, a figure higher than it should be since many people bitten by Coral Snakes do not recognize them as venomous.

DURATION OF LIFE IN CASES OF UNTREATED, FATAL BITE. Demise may occur after any time from one minute to over a month after the bite, according to the reported scientific literature. Most deaths occur within 24 hours, very rarely after one week's survival. Deaths after 24 hours from bites of U. S. species are reputedly seldom due to the effects of hemopathogens, but rather to the neurotoxic effects, or to secondary complications not directly attributable to the venom itself (e.g., septicemia, gangrene, etc.).

8. Cause of Deaths from Snakebite

Despite the alarming and excruciatingly painful effects of the hemopathogens in snake venom, it is evident that in most cases the direct cause of death may be attributed to the more subtle effects of the neurotoxins, through inhibition of heart action and/or respiration.

9. After-Effects in Survivors from Snakebite

Permanent after-effects from snakebite are rare. Inexpert treatment, either in first aid or subsequently, is responsible for almost all permanent after-effects (clinical sequellae). Necrosis and damage to nerves, tendons or blood vessels, as in any wound treatment, may produce permanent tissue changes. Gangrene resulting from over-tight or over-prolonged use of tourniquets may necessitate amputations. But, only in the most severe cases is there evidence of permanent tissue changes due to the effects of the venom. In such cases damage to the kidneys, spleen, and liver, or even to the intestinal wall, may be involved. And, according to Shannon (1957: 139), "an anticipated sequela to a bite from a Coral Snake would be emotional instability for several months to a year following the bite."

PART VI

GENERAL PRECAUTIONS AGAINST SNAKEBITES

A. SEASON OF THE YEAR

Outdoorsmen should be especially on guard during the spring against snakebites because it is at this time of the year that snakes possess their greatest quantities of venom. During winter they store up large amounts of venom, and when they come out of hibernation they go into an upsurge of metabolic activity when they are extremely hungry and are searching for prey. Therefore, any person bitten by a snake in the spring will risk having injected into his body (the victim's) a larger than the usual quantity of venom.

During the late summer and fall months, when snakes have been actively feeding, they have less time to store up large quantities of venom. Thus, when a person is bitten at this season, the amount of venom likely to be injected at the time of the bite is less than would be the case were the victim bitten in the spring.

B. TIME OF THE DAY

Poisonous snakes for the most part are nocturnal animals, and do most of their hunting for food during the hours of darkness or dusk. Therefore, since people are most likely to be bitten at such hours when snakes are abroad and alert, it is recommended that people AVOID walking about in snake-infested country at twilight, during the night, and shortly after sunrise.

C. DANGER OF SNAKE DEN AREAS

Dens are places where snakes hibernate during the winter, such as holes in the ground, crevices in rocks, caves, et cetera. Snakes select as dens places that are below the frost line of the ground, and places which offer them protection from observation.

Snakes are not particularly numerous in the den areas except (a) in the spring when they are coming out of hibernation, and (b) in the fall when they are going into hibernation. When snakes are NOT in hibernation, and are NOT hunting, they tend to seek shelter of some sort. At such times they may commonly be encountered under ground surface cover such as rocks, old boards, logs, piles of debris, et cetera.

D. OBSERVATIONAL PRECAUTIONS

Persons walking in snake-infested country (most outdoor areas may be considered potentially snake-infested) should observe the following general precautions:

1. Do *NOT* put hands (gloved or ungloved) in places where a bite might occur by an unseen snake (e.g., under boards or logs, around and under rocks);

2. Do *NOT* step into such areas of danger in bare feet, or wearing sandals or other footwear giving no protection against bites;

3. Do *NOT* sit down without first looking around;

4. Do *NOT* step blithely over a log, rock or other object without making a preliminary examination of what is on the other side;

5. Do *NOT* turn boards, limbs, or chunks of wood or

debris *away* from you, but instead turn them *toward* you so that they can shield you from the bite of a snake possibly lying underneath;

6. Do *NOT* handle a freshly-killed venomous snake, but use a stick if necessary to manipulate it, for it may still bite reflexly;

7. Do *NOT* camp near piles of brush, rocks or other debris where snakes might hide;

8. Do *NOT* gather firewood or other objects at night when you cannot see clearly all around the area where you step and reach;

9. Do *NOT* sleep on the ground if it can be avoided;

10. Do *NOT* walk close beside a rock wall or ledge where unseen snakes may be hiding; stay a few feet away from it, or inspect it carefully as you walk along.

E. IMPORTANCE OF COMPANIONS

Never hike alone in snake-infested country; always have a companion along. The reasons for this precaution are as follows:

1. No person alone in the field, and bitten by a snake, can perform satisfactorily on himself the necessary first aid measures: application of tourniquet, multiple incisions, and suction at the site of the bite. Any bitten individual attempting self-administration of first aid necessarily has to exert himself physically, a most undesirable situation because such increased activity only hastens the spread of the venom. Therefore, it is imperative that a companion be along to perform the first aid ministrations as required.

2. Also, a companion should be along for the purpose of trying to catch, kill and examine the offending snake in order to determine whether or not it is venomous.

3. The bitten person should receive medical help as quickly as possible. Either a physician should be called to the scene, or the victim be carefully transported to the closest hospital or doctor's office. This cannot be done safely unless someone is along with the victim.

F.   VALUE OF WEARING PROTECTIVE GARMENTS

Persons hiking and climbing in snake-infested areas should wear protective garments over their hands and feet. These items must be thick and firm enough so that a snake cannot bite through them. The reason for this precaution is that most bites are on the hands or forearms, or on the feet and legs below the knee.

For protection of the hands and forearms, heavy leather gloves with gauntlets are advised.

For protection of the feet and legs, thick leather shoes and leather or fine mesh wire puttees are recommended. Boots reaching to the knees, of course, would also satisfy the requirement, but the leather must be heavy to be effective. At least one make of field boot is advertised (Gokey Snake Boot) as affording complete protection over the area covered. (Gokey Co., 94 E. 4th St., St. Paul 1, Minn.)

G.   SNAKEBITE KITS

Any person(s) hiking in snake-infested areas should carry one of the commercially available "Snakebite Kits," or its equivalent in home prepared materials. The procedure for using the kit materials shall be discussed in detail in Part VIII.

At the present time three commercial kits are available on the American market: (1) The Venex Snakebite Pocket Kit sold by the E. D. Bullard Company of San Francisco, California; (2) The Compak Snakebite Kit sold by the Cutter Laboratories of Berkeley, California (Fig. 14); and

(3) the Dudley Snakebite Kit sold by the Flack-Hendrick Company of San Antonio, Texas.

As illustrated below, the commercial kits are inexpensive, very compact and handy, and can be purchased at,

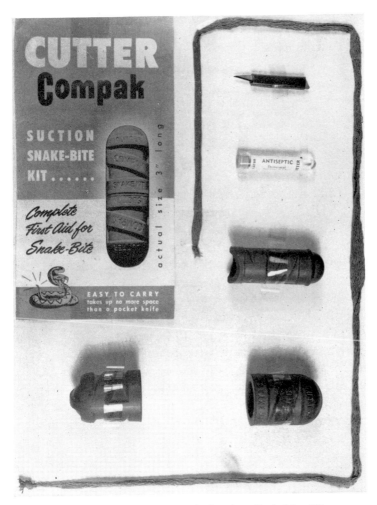

Fig. 14. CUTTER Compak Suction Snakebite Kit.

or ordered from, most retail drug stores. All persons engaged in outdoor work, especially zoologists and others on field trips in potentially or actually snake-infested country, should carry some sort of snakebite kit.

The basic materials contained in the commercial kits, and which should be in the homemade kit, are as follows:

1. Tourniquet

By definition, a tourniquet (from the French word *tourner*, meaning to turn) is a device for arresting bleeding. More specifically, it consists of some rope-like material, placed around the circumference of an extremity, and twisted until the major artery beneath is compressed to the point where the circulation distal to the tourniquet is reduced to the desired degree required for controlling severe hemorrhage. As shall be discussed subsequently in Part VIII, in snakebite cases the tourniquet is employed not to arrest bleeding, but to impede the flow of lymph in the subcutaneous tissues. Arrest of arterial bleeding ordinarily is highly undesirable in the treatment of snakebite, and thus the tourniquet is applied relatively loosely.

In *commercial kits*, the tourniquet usually is a rope-like piece of webbing, or equivalent material. In *homemade kits*, the tourniquet may be a piece of soft narrow rope or clothesline, or a narrow piece of rubber tubing. A broad tourniquet band (e.g., 1-2 inches wide) is better than a narrow one as the wider tourniquets cause less subcutaneous injury, especially to underlying vessels. The tourniquets in most commercial snakebite kits are considered to be too narrow.

In an emergency, when neither commercial nor homemade kits are at hand, a tourniquet can be made out of a long sock, a cravat, a belt, a handkerchief, or by tearing any cloth garment into a suitable strip.

2. Antiseptic

By definition, an antiseptic is any solution or substance which, when applied to any topical surface (i.e., the skin), serves to destroy bacteria present on the surface. As related later in Part VIII, before making the multiple skin incisions necessary in the procedure for treating snakebites, the skin should be rendered as clean as possible to minimize the possibility of secondary wound infection.

In all *commercial kits*, a small vial or tube of some standard antiseptic (e.g., iodine) is always included. In *homemade kits*, a small, tight bottle can be included containing any one of a number of antiseptics purchasable at any drugstore. Satisfactory solutions are iodine, S.T. 37, mercurochrome, alcohol, or one of the well-known mercurial preparations (e.g., Mercresin, Merthiolate, Metaphen).

In an emergency, when neither commercial nor homemade kits are at hand, the cleanliness of the skin can be considerably improved by using soap and water (if soap is available) or just clean water. In this case, the cleansed skin areas are dried with the cleanest cloth material available before the incisions are made. Or, as a last resort device, when neither water nor soap and antiseptics are handy, perhaps the best procedure is to flame-heat the knife point or blade to be used for making the multiple incisions. A knife so treated will be relatively sterile, and will minimize the possibility of introducing skin surface bacteria into the cuts.

3. Cutting Instrument

To make the multiple skin incisions mentioned above, a procedure to be discussed in detail in Part VIII, obviously it is necessary to employ some cutting instrument.

In *commercial kits*, a small, sharp surgical blade is always included. It may, or may not, be in a sterile package. In *homemade kits*, a clean blade of some sort, such as a razor blade or small knife, must be included. It can be carried in a sterile cloth or paper wrap, or inside a small bottle containing some antiseptic (e. g., alcohol).

In an emergency, when neither commercial nor homemade kits are at hand, the First Aider must fall back on his resources. In such situations, a satisfactory cutting instrument may be a jack-knife, a sharp-edged piece of heavy glass, et cetera.

If a sterile blade is available, it can be used directly without further attention. However, if the blade is not sterile, before it is employed it should be cleaned by the First Aider with the best available technique.

4. Suction Cups

In aspirating venom-containing lymph from the subcutaneous tissue spaces, through the mutiple cuts made as described above, two procedures are available: oral suction or so-called suction cups. For reasons to be discussed later in Part VIII, oral suction is contraindicated if the First Aider doing the sucking has any cuts or abrasions in the mouth, or any bleeding point in the stomach. For this reason, if a choice is possible, the use of commercial suction cups is the recommended procedure.

In *commercial kits* (as in Figure 14), usually three suction cups are provided. When the cups are compressed, the open ends placed over individual cuts, and then the finger pressure making the compression is released, a considerable amount of suction is provided. It is well to moisten the open end to improve suction. In *homemade kits*, a First Aider could substitute a glass or rubber aspirating syringe, or even a piece of large-diameter rubber tubing. In use of the latter device, one end of the tubing is placed over the incised areas, the other end in the mouth, and then oral suction is made. If, say, a tube six to eight inches long is so used, there should be little danger of getting venom into the first aider's mouth providing the end touching the skin is never (by mistake) reversed and placed in the mouth. The danger of getting venom in the mouth could be reduced still further by placing a loose plug of cotton or coarse cloth into the tube near the oral end.

In field emergencies where no mechanical suction device is available in any kit (commercial or homemade), and no satisfactory alternative can be found or improvised in the field, there is only one recourse, to employ oral suction.

H.   ARTIFICIAL BODILY IMMUNITY AGAINST VENOM

By taking injections or "shots," immunity can be developed against the harmful effects of any one specific poisonous venom *if the venom is injected in repeated small quantities over a specified period of time.* In actual clinical practice, this is standard immunological procedure although not often specifically used for snake poisons.

Despite the superficial appearance of infallibility, this sort of preventative has certain inherent disadvantages rendering it impractical for the average individual. These disadvantages are:

1. Such immunity can be developed only against specific types of venom.

2. The risks associated with this sort of immunological procedure are excessive for the reason that anaphylactic reactions of varying degrees of seriousness are known to be

incurred unpredictably after either a short or long exposure to the venom. The resistance may well be diminished rather than increased.

3. Even if the procedure is successfully carried out *with no side reactions*, to remain effective the immunity must be maintained by regular, periodic "booster" injections. Immunity is lost promptly after cessation of maintenance injections.

4. Damage to the kidneys and liver often results from repeated exposure to snake venom. These possible complications are serious potentialities because renal and hepatic function may become permanently impaired. Significant diminution of liver functional capacity is especially hazardous to any individual because his body's ability to detoxify venom may be seriously impaired. Thus, should a person in this state be bitten by a venomous snake, the hazards of morbidity and mortality are considerably increased, and a fatal outcome is a much more likely possibility even with what would otherwise be adequate first aid and/or medical treatment.

5. Ordinarily one never knows ahead of time whether or not he will be bitten by a poisonous snake, or, more importantly, what kind of poisonous snake will be involved. Only complete knowledge or assurance of the kind of offending snake would make the immunization procedure worth while. Thus, for the most part, only professional snake handlers qualify for immunization.

I. CONTROL

Thorough discussions of control methods with the objective of reducing number of snakes may be found in Gloyd (1944), Stickel (1953) and P. W. Smith (1953). The recommended methods include, for example, techniques involving poison, traps, predation, snake-proof fencing, and removal of food and cover.

On rare occasion interest is expressed in control methods with the objective of increasing rather than decreasing the number of snakes in a given area. No discussions of appropriate techniques to this end have appeared in the literature. In general we can state that the basic considerations would be provision of: (1) suitable shelter for warm months of the year, (2) food, (3) water, and (4) sites for hibernation. Consult Oliver (1955) for general information on hibernation, water and shelter requirements, and H. M. Smith (1953) for recommendations on food.

PART VII

RECOGNITION OF POISONOUS
SNAKES AND THEIR BITES

There are two major ways for First Aiders to go about getting the information necessary for recognition of a venomous snake bite case: examination of the snake, and examination of the bitten person.

A. EXAMINATION OF THE SNAKE

If the snake can be caught, killed, and examined, it is possible by direct examination to determine whether it is poisonous or non-poisonous. The following anatomical observations are useful in this connection, and constitute DIRECT diagnostic evidence:

(APPROXIMATELY IN THEIR ORDER OF IMPORTANCE)

1. **Front Fangs** (Figs. 5, 6, 8, 9, 13).——**RELIABLE SIGN WHEN OBSERVED**

Coral snakes (poisonous) have FIXED FRONT fangs. Pit Vipers (all poisonous) have MOVABLE FRONT FANGS. In the absence of front fangs, a snake may reliably be regarded as non-poisonous. However, the fangs may not be readily recognized by a novice, and other means of verification of poisonousness and non-poisonousness may thus be desirable.

2. Pits (Figs. 11, 12).——**RELIABLE SIGN WHEN OBSERVED**

These facial pits (which suggest large nostrils, but are not) are readily recognized when present. They are found only in Pit Vipers, all of which are poisonous. Coral Snakes, as well as their mimics, do *not* have such pits.

3. Rattles (Figs. 3, 12).——**RELIABLE SIGN WHEN OBSERVED**

These tail appendages are observed only in the Pit Viper group—not in Coral Snakes. However, some Pit Vipers do not possess rattles at all, and those that do (Rattlesnakes only) may not have enough of a rattle to provide assurance of identification. Young snakes have only a "button" which is not a true rattle, and snakes of any age may lose all of the rattle except the basal segment which by itself does not rattle. Growth of a noise-making mechanism by the addition of another segment to the rattle requires two or three weeks' time after the loss of the rattle, or but a few days after birth.

4. Skin Color Patterns.——**RELIABLE SIGN WHEN OBSERVED**

All states in the United States are inhabited by one or more deadly venomous species of snake, although in several states the snakes barely cross the border. Large areas in the northern part of the country are inhabited by no venomous species, or by but one. The accompanying map (Fig. 15) indicates these areas.

The species having the widest ranges are the Coral Snakes (Fig 16), Copperhead (Fig. 17), Cottonmouth (Fig. 18), Pigmy Rattlesnake (Fig. 19), Massasauga (Fig. 20), Timber Rattlesnake (Fig. 21), Eastern Diamondback Rattlesnake (Fig. 22), Prairie Rattlesnake (Fig. 23), West-

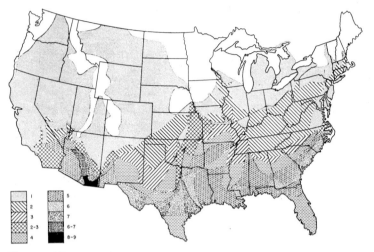

Fig. 15. Number of species of venomous snakes occurring in various parts of the United States.

ern Diamondback Rattlesnake (Fig. 24), and Mojave Rattlesnake (Fig. 25). The illustrations and range maps shown for these species will aid in identification of the snakes responsible for at least 90 per cent of the snake bite cases incurred in the United States. It must nevertheless be admitted that although herpetologists (snake specialists) invariably can distinguish poisonous from non-poisonous snakes by studying the skin color pattern, for all other persons (including First Aiders), this is not a satisfactory diagnostic tool *except in the instance of Coral Snakes.*

Pit Vipers. These patterns are too numerous and complex to be remembered and used accurately by laymen and First Aiders. *UNRELIABLE SIGN EXCEPT FOR EXPERTS.*

Coral Snakes. These snakes have such a striking and characteristic skin color pattern that, once seen in an ac-

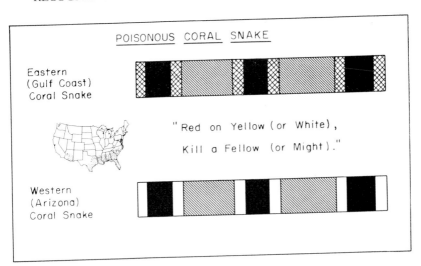

POISONOUS CORAL SNAKE

Eastern
(Gulf Coast)
Coral Snake

"Red on Yellow (or White) ,

Kill a Fellow (or Might)."

Western
(Arizona)
Coral Snake

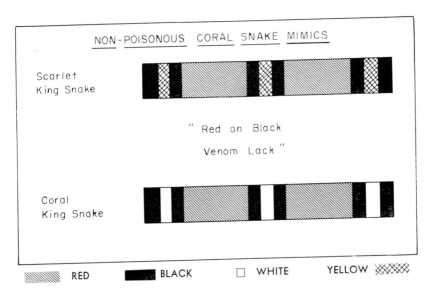

NON-POISONOUS CORAL SNAKE MIMICS

Scarlet
King Snake

" Red on Black

Venom Lack "

Coral
King Snake

RED   BLACK   □ WHITE   YELLOW

Fig. 16. Skin color patterns of Coral Snakes and their mimics
found in the United States. Insert map shows range of the two
species of Coral Snakes in the United States.

tual specimen, the pattern can be remembered and utilized by First Aiders in identifying them. *RELIABLE SIGN.*

CORAL SNAKES (Poisonous, Fig. 16) have fairly wide red bands bordered by narrower *yellow* (or white) bands.

CORAL SNAKE MIMICS (Non-poisonous, Fig. 16) show similar red bands bordered by narrow *black* bands. "Ditty" for remembering the differentiation:

> "Red on Yellow (or white)
> Kill a fellow (or might).
> Red on black,
> Venom lack."

Fig. 17. Copperhead and range thereof in the United States. (Adapted from Ditmars and Stickel.)

Fig. 18. Cottonmouth and range thereof. (Adapted from Ditmars and Stickel.)

Fig. 19. Pigmy Rattlesnake and range thereof. (Adapted from Klauber.)

Fig. 20. Massassauga and range thereof. (Adapted from Klauber.)

Fig. 21. Timber Rattlesnake and range thereof. (Adapted from Klauber.)

Fig. 22. Eastern Diamondback Rattlesnake and range thereof.
(Adapted from Klauber.)

Fig. 23. Prairie Rattlesnake and range thereof in the United States
(Adapted from Stickel and Klauber.)

Fig. 24. Western Diamondback Rattlesnake and range thereof in
the United States. (Adapted from Klauber.)

Fig. 25. Mojave Rattlesnake and range thereof in the United States.
(Adapted from Klauber.)

5. Scale Pattern on the Under-Surface of Tail.——NOT A WHOLLY RELIABLE SIGN

Some, but not all, species of poisonous snakes have a single row of scales covering at least a large part of the under-surface of their tails. All Pit Vipers have such single scales, but Coral Snakes possess two rows of scales throughout the tail as do virtually all non-poisonous snakes. Rare non-poisonous snakes also have a single row of scales on the under-surface of the tail. Only an expert could reliably differentiate venomous and non-venomous snakes by the arrangement of scales under the tail.

For a diagram of a snake with a complete single row of scales on the under-surface of the tail, see Figure 26-A. All such snakes, with few exceptions, are poisonous.

For a diagram of a snake with a complete double row of scales on the under-surface of the tail, see Figure 26-B. All such snakes, except the Coral Snakes, are non-poisonous.

For a diagram of a snake with a single row of scales on part of the tail and a double row on the rest of the tail, see Figure 26-C. All such snakes, with few exceptions, are poisonous.

6. Shape of Head.——NOT A RELIABLE SIGN

The head configurations of snakes vary so much, and are so easily confused, that observation of this characteristic is NOT a useful means of differentiation of poisonous from non-poisonous snakes. Not all venomous snakes, even the Pit Vipers, have especially triangular heads, and many harmless snakes have distinctly triangular heads. There *is* a difference in shape, but it is reliable as a means of differentiation only for experts.

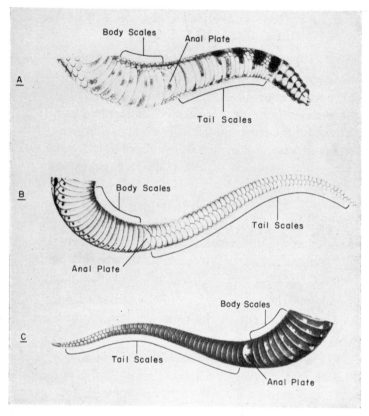

Fig. 26. Basic patterns of scales on the under surfaces of snakes, poisonous and non-poisonous.

A. SINGLE row of scales on the under-side of the tail. Found mostly in poisonous snakes—e.g., Rattlesnakes, as illustrated. (Adapted from Hallowell.)

B. DOUBLE row of scales on the under-side of tail. Found mostly in non-poisonous snakes—e.g., Garter Snake, as illustrated. (Adapted from Hallowell.)

C. Combination of numerous SINGLE scales, and of DOUBLE rows of scales, on the under-side of tail. Found mostly in poisonous snakes—e.g., Cottonmouth, as illustrated. (Adapted from Baird.)

7. Snake Noises.——NOT A RELIABLE SIGN

A "rattling" sound can be made by harmless snakes in several ways, such as by wiggling the end of the tail vigorously in dry leaves or against some resonant object. The harmless Bull Snake also produces an astonishingly rattle-like noise by forceful exhalation of air past a vibrating cartilage located at the upper end of the trachea.

Rattlesnakes produce noise almost exclusively by rapidly wiggling the end of the tail, thus shaking the rattle. Many harmless snakes would also produce a rattle-like sound in *exactly* the same manner if they had a rattle, for they do possess the same neuro-muscular capacity that Rattlesnakes do, vigorously wiggling the tip of the tail when annoyed. If the wiggling tail-tip happens to be lying among dead leaves or on some other resonant medium, a remarkably rattle-like sound is produced.

Noises mimicking "snake noises" also may be produced by the play of the wind on dry ground vegetation, by small animals (e.g., gophers) moving through dry grass or brush, and by many other means. Not only are rattling sounds that may be heard an unreliable indicator of a snake, but not always does a rattlesnake "rattle" before striking.

We can summarize these remarks by observing that neither noises heard, nor their absence, can be relied upon to any reasonable degree as an indicator of either the presence or absence of venomous snakes.

B. EXAMINATION OF THE BITTEN PERSON

There are several bodily signs which, if observed, are useful to First Aiders in deciding whether or not the victim was bitten by a poisonous snake. These signs constitute INDIRECT diagnostic evidence.

1. Bite Pattern.——NOT A RELIABLE SIGN

When a snake bites a person, the main physical altera-
tion is the production of puncture wounds by the teeth
(including the fangs, if present). Since venomous snakes
have teeth in rows on both the upper and lower jaws, in
addition to the fangs at the front of the upper jaw, the
bite usually produces punctures or scratches from numerous small teeth as well as from the fangs. So, it is difficult
to determine whether any of the wounds were caused by
fangs as opposed to the other teeth. Perfect bite patterns
may be diagnosed rather easily, as described below, but
unfortunately perfect patterns are rarely encountered.
They are not seen if the snake strikes a glancing blow,
or if the bitten part is jerked away while the snake is holding on.

a. If the bite involves only FRONT FANGS (which
always means a poisonous snake), the bite pattern on the
victim will approximate the sort of skin appearance diagrammed in Figure 27-A.

b. If the bite involves FRONT FANGS plus some
teeth scratches, the bite pattern on the victim will approximate the sort of skin appearance diagrammed in Figure
27-B.

c. In cases where the victim has been bitten by a non-
poisonous snake, which means teeth marks but no puncture wounds from fangs, the bite pattern on the victim
will approximate the sort of skin appearance diagrammed
in Figure 27-C.

In summary, since poisonous and non-poisonous snakes
may produce skin bite patterns that are much alike in appearance, their similarity makes it difficult for First Aiders
to use these patterns as a diagnostic tool.

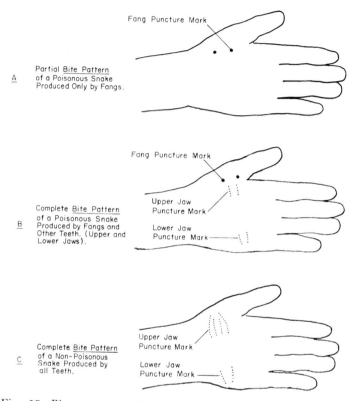

A — Partial <u>Bite Pattern</u> of a Poisonous Snake Produced Only by Fangs.

Fang Puncture Mark

Fang Puncture Mark

B — Complete <u>Bite Pattern</u> of a Poisonous Snake Produced by Fangs and Other Teeth. (Upper and Lower Jaws).

Upper Jaw Puncture Mark

Lower Jaw Puncture Mark

C — Complete <u>Bite Pattern</u> of a Non-Poisonous Snake Produced by all Teeth.

Upper Jaw Puncture Mark

Lower Jaw Puncture Mark

Fig. 27. Bite patterns of poisonous and non-poisonous snakes.

2. Pain.——GENERALLY A RELIABLE SIGN

a. *Non-poisonous Snakebite Cases*

The saliva and tooth-made wounds of harmless snakes may produce mild, local pain or discomfort in the bite area. But, even when present, it rarely persists, and does not spread. Thus, if a person is bitten by a snake, and does NOT develop much local pain in the bite area, the victim can be presumed to have been bitten by a non-poisonous snake (providing other symptoms have not developed).

b. *Poisonous Snakebite Cases (Pit Vipers and Coral Snakes)*

Almost always, persons bitten by poisonous snakes develop immediately or very soon after the bite, deep, violent, burning pain at the site of the bite. If the venomous snake is a Pit Viper, the pain generally spreads rapidly. In cases of bite by Coral Snakes, the pain remains local and does not spread. The bites from a few forms of Rattlesnakes frequently do not cause much pain, whereas bites from types that usually do cause pain will not do so if the dose of the venom is very large, because in large quantities the venom inhibits the activity of the pain receptors instead of stimulating them.

3. Swelling.——GENERALLY A RELIABLE SIGN (Not for Coral Snakes)

a. *Non-poisonous Snakebite Cases*

The saliva from non-poisonous snakes upon entering the subcutaneous tissues of the victim rarely produces swelling in the area of the bite. But, if the swelling does occur in such cases, it remains localized around the bite area, and does not spread.

b. *Poisonous Snakebite Cases (Pit Vipers)*

This venom produces marked soft tissue swelling in the bite area. It starts at the site of the bite usually within three to five minutes (rarely delayed for an hour or more), and then generally spreads rapidly towards the trunk. This is true whether the bite is on an extremity, or even on the face or head.

c. *Poisonous Snakebite Cases (Coral Snakes)*

Interestingly enough, due to the absence of cytolysins in Coral Snake venom as contrasted with the venom of Pit

Vipers which has cytolysins, there is no significant swelling in the tissues of victims bitten by Coral Snakes.

4. Miscellaneous Symptoms.——RELIABLE WHEN OBSERVED

Sometimes the sharp pain and/or swelling characteristic of most snakebites do not develop, at least not within the customary test period of 15 minutes after the bite occurs. If other alarming symptoms, as listed below, do develop, the bite may be considered to be that of a venomous snake even in the absence of swelling and sharp pain. Still other means of identifying a viperine bite may be employed by the physician as necessary (see Part IX).

a. *Weakness*

Care should be taken to distinguish between fear-induced and venom-produced weakness.

b. *Giddiness*

Use care in diagnosis as for 4-a immediately above.

c. *Paralysis, Twitching, or Numbness*

Often a marked numbness, particularly about the lips, mouth and tongue, may occur very soon after the bite. Tingling of the skin may be felt in some cases, also muscular twitching.

Summary. The presence of local tissue swelling and/or pain at the site of a snakebite is a *RELIABLE SIGN*. If *no* significant local swelling, pain, or other alarming symptoms develop within a short period of time (perhaps 15 to 30 minutes), the bite can be identified positively as having been inflicted by a non-poisonous snake. Definite swelling that spreads indicates a bite by a poisonous Pit Viper. Deep pain alone, without swelling, indicates a bite by a poisonous Coral Snake.

PART VIII

FIRST AID MEASURES IN TREATING POISONOUS AND NON-POISONOUS SNAKEBITE CASES

The measures listed below should be carried out and continued by the First Aider:

* **UNTIL** it has been definitely determined that the bite was by a non-poisonous snake;

* **UNTIL,** in cases where it is definitely established that the bite was by a poisonous snake, the pain and swelling have subsided or have stopped spreading;

* **UNTIL,** in either case situation, medical help has been secured, and therapeutic case responsibility has been transferred by the First Aider to the physician called.

A. KEEPING BODILY METABOLISM AT A MINIMUM

Any increase in physical activity only increases bodily metabolism, which, in turn, promotes the rapidity of the spread of the venom by reason of speeding-up the arterial-venous and lymphatic circulation.

Specific measures for the First Aiders to use in retarding bodily metabolism are as follows:

1. Position

The bitten person should *immediately* lie down, and the bitten part (usually an extremity) be placed in a position *lower* than the rest of the body. Keep the victim dry by having him lie on coats, or on a blanket, if available. In selecting a place to lie down, precautions should be taken to insure absence of snakes from the immediate vicinity.

2. Muscular Activity

Since muscular activity is perhaps the most common cause of increased bodily metabolism, be sure that the victim remains quiet, and does not move. Do not allow the victim to walk around while undergoing first aid treatment, while awaiting medical help called to the scene of the accident, or while being transported to some nearby dwelling to which medical help may have been summoned.

3. Fear and Emotional Excitement

Bodily metabolism also can be activated by fear and emotional excitement. The best reassurance to the victim is prompt, intelligent first aid treatment, and confidence in the knowledge that in the past 10 years the actual number of fatalities from rattlesnake bites in the United States has been reduced to about 1 in 30, and that the ratio of fatalities is much lower for moccasin bites. Fear alone can be fatal even if the bite is of the harmless variety.

4. Alcohol

Do not give the victim alcohol; it is NOT good "snakebite medicine" as it only speeds-up the internal bodily metabolism thereby increasing the rate of spread of the venom in the body.

5. Food

When food is eaten, in either liquid or solid form, the bodily metabolism is increased. Therefore, until medical attention has been secured, snakebite victims should NOT consume any form of food (liquid or solid) as the increased metabolism only serves to speed the spread of venom in the body. Water may be given as desired.

B.   MECHANICAL REMOVAL OF VENOM FROM THE SUBCUTANEOUS TISSUES*

Once venom gets into the arterial or venous circulation, it is carried to the liver where the body detoxifies and removes it. Venom will kill the victim if the dose injected into the tissues is massive, and if the liver is overwhelmed and cannot detoxify the venom rapidly enough. However, if the venom gets into the arterial and venous circulation slowly enough, it will be delivered to the liver at such a decreased rate that the liver can detoxify it rapidly enough to avoid fatal complications, and the victim will likely live.

Fortunately, the venom in most snakebites is NOT injected directly into arteries or veins. Rather, in most cases the venom is injected into the subcutaneous soft tissues (below the skin). The soft tissues are drained mainly by the so-called lymphatic circulatory channels located just below the skin. No matter how deeply the fangs may penetrate, the venom flows with the lymph toward the superficial subcutaneous spaces.

Lymph is a yellowish-white fluid existing in and around all subcutaneous and other bodily tissues. It is a fluid formed by filtration of the blood through capillary walls. More specifically, lymph is a blood serum derivative which lacks cells because these were filtered out. The absence of red blood cells accounts for its pale, serum-like appearance. It is important to know something about lymph and its flow inasmuch as lymph (not blood) is the vehicle carrying the venom in the body. The object of the three basic first

*See Critical Comment, page 143.

aid procedures, discussed hereafter, is to remove mechanically as much venom-bearing lymph as is possible.

Students wishing to read about the anatomical considerations involved here are referred to standard medical
anatomy texts. As brought out in these sources, the lymphatic vessel system arises in the lymphatic capillary plex-

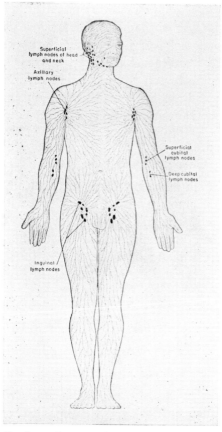

Fig. 28. Distribution of some of the superficial lymph nodes and
lymph vessels. (Courtesy, *Blakiston's New Gould Medical Dic-
tionary*, The Blakiston Company, Inc., 1949.)

uses in both the deep and superficial subcutaneous soft tissues (Fig. 28). The plexuses are connected with afferent lymphatic vessels entering lymph nodes from which efferent lymph vessels pass to a series of lymph nodes still farther cephalad (towards the head), eventually draining into the thoracic duct or the right lymphatic duct. These two structures lie deep inside the thorax and neck, alongside the esophagus. The *thoracic duct* collects the lymph flow from all parts of the body except from the right side of the head and neck and thorax, the right upper extremity, and the convex surface of the liver. The *right lymphatic duct* collects the lymph from all other organs and tissues which do not drain into the thoracic duct. Eventually, both the thoracic duct and the right lymphatic duct drain into the venous circulation in the vicinity of the subclavian and internal jugular veins.

Fortunately, it is possible to employ certain first aid techniques which make it possible mechanically to remove a considerable amount of the venom since it lies in the lymph spaces in the subcutaneous tissues in the vicinity of the snakebite or trunkward therefrom. These measures include actual sucking or aspiration of the lymph with its venom content and not the removal of blood.

The basic three first aid measures which currently are considered to constitute accepted emergency treatment in cases of snakebite are listed below; they are always used in the order stated.

1. Tourniquet

Tourniquets can only be used in cases of snakebites on an extremity. The tourniquet is placed immediately a few inches above the site of the bite, and should be tight enough to obstruct venous and lymphatic circulation, but not arterial circulation. One test is to check the pulse at the wrist in case of a bite of the upper extremity, or at the ankle in case of a bite involving the lower extremity. The pulse may be *slightly* weakened at these points, but should not be conspicuously weakened or stopped. A continuous check should be made to be sure that the tourniquet does not become too tight or too loose. A *narrow* tourniquet would have to be drawn somewhat tighter to effect the desired constriction than would a broad tourniquet, and should be loosened periodically. A *broad* tourniquet properly applied does not need to be loosened for hours at a time except at the cessation of treatment, or to move the tourniquet to a more proximal site on the bitten extremity.

It is also recommended that as an additional precaution, if the bite has occurred at a 2 (or more)-bone level (as on the hand or foot, forearm or lower leg), an additional tourniquet be placed on the nearest proximal one-bone level (as on the upper arm or thigh).

The logic of the tourniquet is so plainly evident that for this very reason it may be misused. Gangrene can result from an over-tight tourniquet that is left on too long. True, a tight tourniquet may be loosened periodically, but there is still the danger of its remaining in place too long. A tight tourniquet left in place as long as 8 or 9 hours is said to cause death; it will cause some tissue damage in as little time as 15 minutes. Many deaths and amputations accompanying snakebite have been shown to have been the effects of over-tight tourniquets, not the venom itself, and undoubtedly many others of the same cause have not been recognized.

2. Multiple Incisions

(See Figure 29–A, B, C.) The purpose of this procedure is to expose the subcutaneous lymph spaces and fluid to

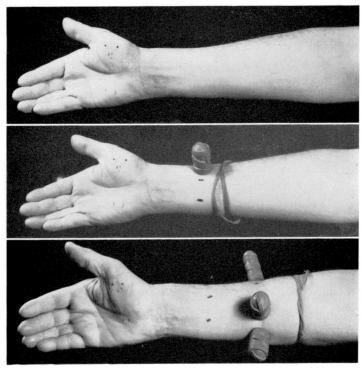

Fig. 29. Successive steps in the first aid treatment of venomous snakebite cases. (Illustration with normal forearm and hand.)

Upper. The bite pattern prior to treatment, showing punctures by fangs and solid teeth of both jaws.

Middle. Early steps in treatment, showing tourniquet in place, the initial ring of multiple incisions, and the use of suction bulbs.

Lower. Later stages showing tourniquet, ring of incisions, and suction bulbs all shifted proximally.

the outside so that, as shall be discussed next under (3), suction through the openings made in the skin can be undertaken, and the venom be removed mechanically from the subcutaneous lymph spaces. If medical assistance can be secured within 10 or 15 minutes, incision should be deferred for the physician. As previously discussed under Snakebite Kits in Part VI, Section G, before making the incisions, it is important to clean the skin as well as possible, and to make the incisions with a cutting device as nearly sterile as possible.

Shallow cuts (⅛ inch deep) should be made through the skin down to the red part, the so-called "quick." Do NOT make deep cuts, even at the site of bite; they are not necessary to expose the lymph spaces, and may injure important subcutaneous nerves, vessels, and tendons.

The cuts should also be made longitudinally; do not make cross-wise or "X" cuts. They are unnecessary, heal slowly, and may do greater damage than longitudinal cuts.

These shallow, longitudinal cuts are to be made in a row or ring around the circumference of the extremity—usually about one inch apart. If there is much blood loss, indicating that a relatively large vessel has been cut, staunch the flow with a compress. It is the *lymph* that is desired, not the blood. Blood will always flow from the fresh cut, but after a time primarily lymph (the yellowish-white fluid) should flow. Abstraction (withdrawal) of large quantities of blood is undesirable, as the patient's general condition may be weakened to an unnecessary and possibly serious extent.

Where the incisions are made depends upon the site of the bite. Generally speaking, with the exceptions to be noted, start the cuts three inches above the bite, or (if the case had advanced before first aid treatment could be started) make the cuts at the crest of the swelling. Incisions should NOT be made in any part of the hand or foot, wrist, or ankle, unless the tissues are sufficiently swol-

len so as to insure that cuts made through the skin cannot
damage underlying tendons, nerves and vessels.

> *Do NOT attempt to cauterize the bite or the
> cuts. Do NOT put chemicals (e.g., potas-
> sium permanganate) or other substances or
> objects (except antiseptics) in or on the
> bite or cuts. Such procedures are con-
> sidered more harmful than beneficial. Some
> chemicals (e.g., potassium permanganate)
> are actually poisonous in themselves.

> **Also, do NOT try to refrigerate the local
> bite area by using some drastic measures
> as ethyl chloride spray. Ice water packs, or
> an ice pack, on the bite area are of no
> known value, and, if continued for more
> than a few minutes, may do considerable
> damage by lowering tissue temperatures be-
> low the minimum the tissues can tolerate.
> Large masses of flesh can be lost by gan-
> grene resulting from low temperature
> alone. Cool water, applied with reasonable
> caution, may have some slight symptomatic
> value.

3. Suction

By sucking over the bite and/or the multiple incisions
(preferably two or three at once) made as described above,
it is possible to remove significant amounts of the venom.
This suction must be made continuously in a sequence
over each cut with only occasional rest periods. Strong
suction is to be avoided. In all cases the bite should be
sucked immediately and for a time thereafter even if the
incisions are deferred for the physician.

The suction can be performed by two techniques. MOUTH SUCTION is often the only method available. It is perfectly safe for the First Aider as long as he does not have bleeding points in the mouth (e.g., sores or cracks in lips, significant bleeding of the dental gums, or sores or cracks on the mucosal surfaces of the inside of the mouth), or in the stomach (e.g., bleeding gastric or duodenal ulcer). The fluid sucked from the wound should be spit out, but what is swallowed is digested by the body and no harm comes from it. It is true that the venom can be absorbed into the body and circulation of the operator if bleeding points do exist. Most First Aiders do not have such bleeding points, and can safely suck out the lymph and venom in snakebite emergencies. Nevertheless, this precaution must always be seriously considered by the First Aider.

SUCTION CUP TECHNIQUE (Figure 29). Because of the possible hazard to the First Aider, who does not always know for sure whether or not he has bleeding points in the lips or mouth or stomach, a highly recommended technique is to do the suction over the multiple incisions using the commercially available suction cups. These cups have a rubber bulb on them, which, by squeezing and then letting go, provide the necessary suction. The cups adhere better to the skin if moistened at the open end, and thus moistening them also promotes better suction force.

**Continuation Treatment. *If the tourniquet is thought to be too tight, each 10 to 15 minutes it should be released for two or three minutes. Then, at the same time, or at intervals required by the progress of the swelling, the tourniquet should be reapplied at a higher level (perhaps 4-6 inches above the site of the previous application), new* *incisions should be made, and suction again be applied—all as described above.*

In case of a bite by a poisonous Pit Viper, where local tissue swelling is a prominent feature, the tourniquet is always applied just proximal to the top or crest of the swelling. When the bite is by a poisonous Coral Snake, where local tissue swelling is NOT a prominent feature, the tourniquet arbitrarily is moved up a few inches anyway at the end of each 20 to 30 minute period.

Should the victim become faint during the first aid regimen, it is permissible and proper for the First Aider to use on the victim one of the commonly employed stimulants. Standard measures of this sort are as follows: cold applications to the forehead, lowering the head below the body or trunk level, smelling salts (e.g., aromatic spirits of ammonia), brisk rubbing or slapping of the skin, et cetera.

C. SENDING FOR MEDICAL ASSISTANCE

The type of medical attention will depend upon the circumstances of the individual snakebite case. If the victim can be transported with assistance to some nearby inhabited dwelling (e.g., a farm house), then perhaps the best procedure is to request an immediate house call there by the physician contacted. Otherwise, especially in serious cases, the physician should be asked to see the victim in the field.

Details regarding locating a physician, and notifying family or near relatives of the victim, shall be considered in Section D which follows.

D. RECOMMENDED GENERAL *FIRST AID PROCEDURE* IN SPECIFIC CASE SITUATIONS

For purposes of illustration, all cases will be presumed to be snakebites on the extremities.

1. The Victim Is Alone

a. THE VICTIM IS *UNCERTAIN* ABOUT THE KIND OF OFFENDING SNAKE: IT MIGHT BE EITHER POISONOUS OR NON-POISONOUS.

(It shall be taken for granted that the victim will have exhausted all reasonable means of reliable determination of the seriousness of the bite—see Part VII.)

Step I

The victim *lies down* at the place where he is bitten, remains perfectly quiet, and in particular *keeps the bitten member as immobile as possible and at a lower level than the body.*

↓

Step II

He *applies a tourniquet* around the bitten extremity *above the site of the bite,* and *sucks the bite.*

↓

Step III

The victim now rests quietly for 10 to 15 minutes with the tourniquet in place.

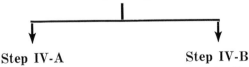

Step IV-A	Step IV-B
If no significant swelling, or pain, or tingling of the scalp, feet, lips or tongue develop	*If significant tingling in peripheral areas, or swelling and /or pain in the area of the*

after this period of time, the victim presumes that the bite was by a NON-poisonous snake. He then starts walking slowly towards the nearest likely habitation.

Step V-A

When the victim has reached a dwelling, he will either (a) be convinced beyond doubt that the snake was harmless, or (b) remain uncertain. If (a) is true, local antiseptics may be applied if so desired. Early report of the bite to a physician is recommended.

Step VI-A

If (b) is true, then the victim should be transported to a

bite, develop after this period of time, the victim presumes that *the bite was by a VENOMOUS snake.* This being the case, *he remains lying perfectly quiet,* and *proceeds as best he can to perform on himself the multiple cuts and suction.*

Step V-B

While p e r f o r m i n g IV-B above, the *victim remains where he is located,* and lies quietly until help arrives or the worst is over. If it appears likely that a long and uncomfortable wait will ensue, and *if there is reasonably nearby a known habitation, the victim should work his way towards the shelter walking with minimal exertion. C A U T I O N. The victim should never attempt to walk for help, or exercise unduly in seeking help, unless it is quite evident that failure to do so would jeopardize survival more than the poison itself.*

Step VI-B

Also while performing IV-B above, *the victim will try to*

physician for further observation and treatment. Nevertheless, the *victim should never attempt to walk for help unless the distance is very short, or unless other factors jeopardize survival even more than the snake poison.* In any case first aid procedures should be followed meticulously.

attract the attention of any passers-by, or of low flying planes overhead, or (if by a lake or river) the boats or fishermen going nearby. Depending on the available facilities, the victim may try to attract attention by using flares, shooting a gun, starting a smoky fire, using a flashlight (if dark), etc. *Any help attracted will try to notify relatives and get medical help.*

b.   THE VICTIM IS *CERTAIN* THAT THE OFFENDING SNAKE IS NON-POISONOUS.

He treats the bite as any other puncture wound.

c.   THE VICTIM IS *CERTAIN* THAT THE OFFENDING SNAKE IS POISONOUS.

He follows, in sequence, Steps I, II, IV-B, V-B, and VI-B as described above.

2.   The Victim Has One Companion

a.   BOTH THE VICTIM AND COMPANION ARE *UNCERTAIN* ABOUT THE KIND OF OFFENDING SNAKE: IT MIGHT BE EITHER POISONOUS OR NON-POISONOUS.

(Here again it is presumed that the companion and victim have exhausted every means in determining the venomousness of the offending snake.)

Step I
As in Step I above, p. 99

Step II
As in Step II above, p. 99, except that the com-

panion does the first aid work—applying the
tourniquet, et cetera.

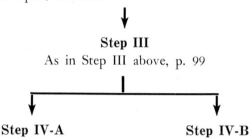

Step III
As in Step III above, p. 99

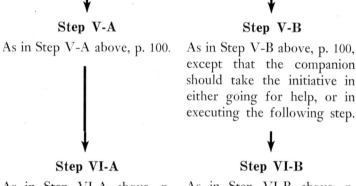

Step IV-A

As in Step IV-A above, p. 99,
except that the companion
(First Aider) assists the victim
in walking toward the nearest
habitation.

Step IV-B

As in Step IV-B above, p. 99,
except that the companion
does the necessary first aid
work.

Step V-A

As in Step V-A above, p. 100.

Step V-B

As in Step V-B above, p. 100,
except that the companion
should take the initiative in
either going for help, or in
executing the following step.

Step VI-A

As in Step VI-A above, p.
100.

Step VI-B

As in Step VI-B above, p.
100, except that the companion does the work necessary
in trying to attract the attention of passers-by.

b. The Victim and Companion Are *CERTAIN*
that the Offending Snake Is Non-Poisonous.

They treat the bite as any other puncture wound.

c. The Victim and Companions Are *CERTAIN* that the Offending Snake Is Poisonous.

Follow, in sequence, Steps I, II, IV-B, V-B, and VI-B as described in 2-a above.

3. The Victim Has Two or More Companions

a. The Victim and Companions Are *UNCERTAIN* As to Whether or Not the Offending Snake Is Poisonous.

(It shall be presumed that the companions have made every effort to try to catch, kill, and identify the offending snake.)

Step I

As in Step I above, p. 99.

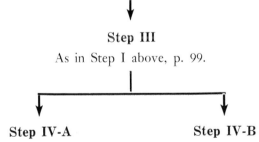

Step II

As in Step II above, p. 99, except that one companion does the first aid work—applying the tourniquet; et cetera.

Step III

As in Step I above, p. 99.

Step IV-A	**Step IV-B**
As in Step IV-A above, p. 99, except that the companions on the spot assist the victim in walking towards the nearest habitation.	At this point, a choice should be made between three possible procedures. (X) It may be decided, especially in very serious cases, *NOT to move*

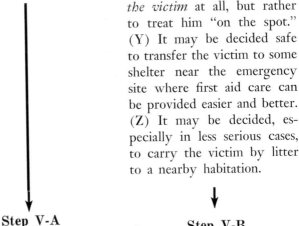

the victim at all, but rather to treat him "on the spot." (Y) It may be decided safe to transfer the victim to some shelter near the emergency site where first aid care can be provided easier and better. (Z) It may be decided, especially in less serious cases, to carry the victim by litter to a nearby habitation.

Step V-A

As in Step V-A above, p. 100.

Step V-B

If (X) above is the choice, one or two c o m p a n i o n s should remain with the victim to perform the first aid treatment as previously described, while the remaining companions leave and seek help. If (Y) above is the choice, first aid treatment is first instituted, and then the victim is transported to the intended shelter. When this point has been reached, one or more of the companions remain performing the necessary first aid work, while the remaining companions go to summon medical help to the shelter. If (Z) above is the choice, the messenger should go immediately for help, the others remaining to assist in

the first aid and transporta-
tion.

Step VI-A	**Step VI-B**
As in Step VI-A above, p. 100.	Following choice (X) above, the victim should be carried to a shelter to which a physician may be summoned, stopping at intervals to continue first aid treatment.

b. THE VICTIM AND COMPANION ARE *CERTAIN* THAT THE OFFENDING SNAKE IS NON-POISONOUS.

The companions treat the bite as any other puncture wound.

c. THE VICTIM AND COMPANIONS ARE CERTAIN THAT THE OFFENDING SNAKE IS POISONOUS.

Follow, in sequence, Steps I, II, IV-B, V-B, and VI-B as described in 3-a above.

PART IX

MEDICAL TREATMENT IN CASES OF SNAKEBITE

Definitive treatment in cases of venomous snakebite naturally is the responsibility and prerogative of the medical man, the physician. But, it is believed that all interested First Aiders should have a cursory but sound acquaintance with the various medical measures that the physician might employ. We have drawn extensively from the remarkably thorough summary by Klauber (1956), and from the invaluable AAAS symposium on *Venoms* (1956), for material in this as well as other sections of this treatise.

It seems to the authors that the various treatments recommended for use in snakebite cases may be considered to fall into three categories: *medical, surgical,* and what might be termed *ectotherapeutic* measures.

1. For centuries man has searched without success for a "medical panacea" for snakebite poisoning (Leake, 1956). Among the many formerly recommended medicinal preparations, administered either orally or topically, but now totally discredited, are potassium permanganate, procaine, magnesium sulfate, gold salts, kerosene, alcohol, ammonia, milk, turpentine, vinegar, tobacco, indigo, lard, olive oil, iodine, salt, gunpowder, alum, epsom salts, mud, snake stones, parts of the snakes, and parts of other animals. Some of these do inactivate venom *in vitro*, but they all fail to do so *in vivo*. In addition, some are just as harmful as the venom, or more so. In recent years, heparin, antihis-

tamine, neostigmine, cortisone, ACTH, India ink and ascorbic acid (Vitamin C), have been tried with but limited success. The one well-tested medication that approaches the ideal is *antivenin*, but this too leaves much to be desired. Newcomers to snakebite therapy that seem to hold much promise are 2 drugs with calcium in the form of calcium gluconate and calcium lactate. Detailed discussions of several of these preparations follow in Part IX.

2. Surgical techniques include tourniquet, incision, drainage, suction, positioning of the body and limbs, cryotherapy, excision, venesection, cauterization, and amputation. These measures shall be discussed later in Part IX. Rarely, it might be mentioned here, should any of the latter five techniques listed above be employed.

3. Ectotherapeutic devices are those exercised externally, on or about the bitten person, but neither topically nor orally. For the most part, these devices are of a superstitious or supernatural character, and of greater ethnic than medical interest. Incantations and charms are the most common variants of such witchcraft; numerous interesting examples are given by Corkill (1956: 336-7) for Africa, and by Ahuja and Singh (1956: 348-9) for India. Undoubtedly certain surgical and medical measures might also be categorized as essentially witchcraft, but our emphasis is not upon the supernatural but upon a category in classification of methods of treatment. The only ectotherapeutic device of repute, as applied to snakebite, is psychotherapy, the value of which appears to be limited largely to the control of anxiety, a factor that can be important in the resistance of the patient to the bite.

✻   ✻   ✻   ✻   ✻

In addition, in these introductory remarks, we wish to express a few general comments on the problem of *verification* of snakebite. On rare occasions, the physician may be uncertain as to whether or not a given case represents an actual snakebite. If the criteria given in Part VII are of insufficient help, the physician's general knowledge usually can provide the necessary assurance. In this connection, there have been reported recently two accessory diagnostic techniques that merit brief comment:

1. Ahuja and Singh (1956: 347) in India have utilized successfully *blood clotting* time as an accessory diagnostic device. We quote from their article:

> In our experience, when a patient arrives for treatment more than half an hour after having been bitten, one can almost certainly rule out viper bite if the blood coagulation (time) is less than 10 minutes. In the absence of neurotoxic symptoms, this simple test is of great help in ruling out the bite of a deadly snake in India.

Whether or not the blood coagulation time test would be equally reliable for North American crotaline snakes, is unknown to us. Certainly the subject seems to merit investigation by North American clinicians and herpetologists.

2. Carhill (1956: 334) has advanced the *evaluation of kidney function* as an accessory diagnostic measure for use in human snakebite cases where verification is difficult. He has stated:

> The appearance of red blood cells and casts in the urine in 25 out of 29 cases of poisoning by cobras or vipers (in Africa), shows the kidney as a delicate indicator of viperine (and presumably also elapid) poisoning.

Here would also seem a fertile field of investigation for other North American clinicians and herpetologists.

❊   ❊   ❊   ❊   ❊

Finally, we take this opportunity to point out that hemopathic poisons do not always produce local swelling. Powerful hemorrhagins are present in the venoms of various foreign species such as the African Boomslang, yet little swelling occurs even in fatal cases (for example, in the death of the late dean of American herpetologists, Karl P. Schmidt). Appearance of alarming signs, such as external bleeding from mucous membranes anywhere (e.g., nose, mouth), from the intestines (as evidenced by bloody stools) or from the kidneys (as evidenced by bloody urine), should be followed immediately by treatment with antivenin. Preferably the antivenin should be specific, but if that is not possible, then it should be for species whose venom provokes the most nearly identical symptoms. All other supportive measures, as described hereinafter, should be utilized.

The cause for the difference in action of the hemorrhagins of Boomslangs and of most other snakes is not known. Fitzsimons (1921) has provided evidence strongly suggesting that it is not so much a difference in venom or in the poisonous principles thereof as it is in site of injection. He found (*op. cit.:* 511-514) that subcutaneous injection of the strongly hemotoxic venom of the African Puff Adder, which normally induces extensive local swelling in animals it bites, is followed by general symptoms and no local swelling, and that only the deeper intramuscular injection produces the "typical" reaction with local swelling. Since the Boomslang has short fangs (it is a rear-fanged snake) it would be likely to inject venom subcutaneously. All case reports of Boomslang bite reveal the *general* pattern of response rather than the *local* pattern.

It is to be assumed, until proved otherwise, that the bite from any snake with hemopathic venom may, if only subcutaneous injection occurred, result in appearance of general symptoms only, and the absence of most local symptoms. This hypothesis is presently under investigation.

A. GENERAL RECOMMENDATIONS (Summary)

Shannon (1956: 407) has succinctly summarized general measures pertinent to sound therapy in snakebite cases. His general recommendations are so clearly and briefly put forth, that we are quoting them verbatim:

"A patient with snakebite should be hospitalized for observation no matter how inconsequential the effects of the bite seem to be. Blood typing should be carried out at once, as hemolysins may shortly alter the protein structure to such an extent that such procedures will become impossible. A urinalysis and a complete blood count should be done. Intravenous saline and blood should be administered if hemoglobinuria or albuminuria is present. Plasma should be given in any case, as the globulin fraction may be of considerable benefit to the patient. The Trendelenburg position should be employed if the patient is in shock, and utilization of the usual vasodepressors may be necessary. Use of a half-gram of calcium chloride may lessen hemolysis. Emboli or cerebral hemorrhages may occur and should be promptly diagnosed. It is becoming increasingly apparent that ACTH, although of some use in combating symptomatology, does not lessen the probability of a fatal issue. Barbiturates and opiates may be used with caution. Draining wounds should be covered with moist packs.

"Considerable caution should be exercised against the use of excessive heat or cold. Tissues in the vicinity of a bite are anoxic, as a result of action by proteolysins and hemolysins present in the venom. If metabolic needs are increased by the application of heat or if the superficial tissues are further damaged by cold, there remains no way of increasing regional blood supply.

"In the case of venom containing a damaging ratio of neurotoxins, considerable emphasis should be placed upon combating central nervous system symptoms, and use of analeptics may be necessary. The supine position should not be used, as laryngeal paralysis may lead to salivary strangulation. An airway may be of some use, and a respirator may be instrumental in carrying a marginal case along until an otherwise lethal excess of venom is detoxified. Likewise an electrophrenic respirator may be of marginal benefit."

B.   CONTINUATION OF STANDARD FIRST AID MEASURES*

The concensus of medical and zoological experts in snakebite treatment is that the *major* therapeutic device remains the standard first aid methods of tourniquet, multiple incisions, and suction. Certainly the bites of all North American snakes, with the possible exception of the Coral Snakes, are best treated by these means. Likewise the bites of most exotic Vipers (both pit and pitless) are amenable to treatment by these means. The bites of the essentially neurotoxic Coral Snakes and the exotic members of the same family (Elapidae) and the Sea Snake family are not, however, readily amenable to mechanical treatment primarily because there is no overt evidence of the location of the venom. In the hemopathic types (the two groups of Vipers) the local effects usually clearly reveal the location of the venom and its progress, thus making possible an efficient and effective use of mechanical treatment.

*See Critical Comment, page 143.

A truly astonishing proportion of the subcutaneous venom can be removed by exercise of these three first aid methods if they are started promptly and maintained continously until the danger period has passed.

So, in most instances, any physician called to attend a snakebite case will very likely see to it that these three standard first aid measures are continued as long as necessary, progressively advancing the longitudinal cuts to keep pace with the swelling (if any). Suction for 20 minutes per hour for the first 5 to 15 or even 24 hours is recommended, depending upon the severity of the symptoms. Suction may be applied to the incisions, as suggested by Shannon (1956: 406) and others, by suction bulbs, breast pumps, or suction machines. Alternating positive and negative pressure, such as might be obtained by use of a Pavex boot, is a highly effective way to remove venom (Shannon, 1956: 406). Free bleeding should not be allowed to continue, although some blood loss is inevitable in the suction treatment. The physician must be guided by the local hemorrhagic condition in judging the merit of further treatment.

In this connection, it is believed desirable to discuss two supplemental therapeutic adjuncts which have been recommended in the past to physicians handling snakebite wounds. Those advocating these adjuncts affirm that the techniques augment lymph flow, and facilitate wound drainage.

Subcutaneous saline injections. According to a few authors, elimination of venom can be facilitated by the subcutaneous injection of normal saline solution in the areas undergoing suction treatment thus augmenting the lymph flow, and thereby assisting the removal of venom from the intercellular spaces. More experienced clinical investigators and practioners, however, doubt that this therapeutic technique is a significant aid, considering the mobilizing effects of the so-called "spreading-factors" in the tissues of the bite area. Shannon, for example, states that in rattlesnake bite cases, the "spreading-factor" content of the venom is sufficient enough so that, in cases of a bitten finger or toe, the venom very rapidly saturates the subcutaneous spaces and almost immediately encircles the digit.

Incision-wound compresses. A few authors have recommended that, between the periods of suction, the multiple incisions should be covered with magnesium sulfate compresses to facilitate drainage of the venom-bearing lymph from the subcutaneous spaces. In serious cases, they have recommended that such compresses be continued for as long as two weeks. Naturally, this sort of medical therapy requires hospitalization of the patient. Again, the concensus of clinicians of widest experience in treating snakebite cases seems to be that such compresses usually are not necessary inasmuch as most of these incision-wounds drain profusely without attempted assistance.

In urging the continuation of mechanical treatment, we should also warn against overtreatment. It is not considered good judgment in adult cases to treat the bite of a small snake (20 inches, or under) of the less formidable species (Copperheads, Cottonmouths, Pigmy Rattlesnakes) with the same exhaustive thoroughness with which the bite of a full-grown rattlesnake may be treated. Some judgment must be exercised by the physician in determining how far he should go with mechanical treatment as well as alternative measures (Shannon, 1956: 406).

At the other extreme, drastic measures may be necessary to treat venomous bites on the trunk where the usual mechanical devices are inapplicable. By experiments upon dogs, Parrish (1956) has reported a method which might be considered for use in selected human snakebite cases. According to his results:

> *IF no antivenin is available;*
>
> *IF the bite is so located on the body that Tourniquets cannot be used (e.g., the trunk);*
>
> *IF the patient is seen by the physician within an hour of the snakebite;*
>
> *IF the site of the bite is such that there are no anatomical contraindications to the suggested maneuver;*

then, excision of an area of skin 7 cm. in diameter, and with removal of all subcutaneous tissue below it, should should be substituted for incision and suction. It is rare indeed that the 4 conditions noted above would occur in humans simultaneously. Nevertheless, such an emergency is possible. The Parrish surgical measure, having been proved valid in animal studies, might seriously be considered for use in such rare cases. If adopted, the procedure clearly would be the more useful the earlier it could be initiated. After one hour (in dogs) it had no superiority over incision and suction.

C.   ANTIVENINS*

The antivenins, if available and if used in time and in sufficient quantity, are sometimes effective in the treatment of poisonous snakebite cases. These preparations are designed for the purpose of neutralizing directly the venom injected into the victim's tissues at the time of the bite by a poisonous snake. The more venom that can be neutralized by this means, the less will remain to produce tissue damage or to be detoxified by bodily processes of the victim alone without therapeutic support.

*See Critical Comment, page 143.

The exact efficacy of the antivenin *versus* mechanical first aid treatment is still a topic of debate. Many authorities maintain that *mechanical treatment* (the three standard first aid measures previously described—tourniquet, multiple incisions, and suction) is a liability because in the hands of most amateurs mechanical treatment is performed in a hesitant, clumsy, ineffective manner without due attention to sterility precautions. Other authorities, however, affirm that *antivenin treatment* may also be a liability inasmuch as in too many cases it is administered too late, in insufficient quantity, and without due precautions as to testing and/or treating the patient for anaphylactic reactions. For reasons heretofore and hereafter discussed, the authors of this monograph remain convinced that both the accepted first aid methods and the antivenin treatment, properly employed and controlled, have ample merit and warrant utilization. Despite the fact that present-day antivenins are probably far from their ultimate perfection, the highly refined products now available seem deserving of particular attention inasmuch as antivenin IS a specific biochemical attack against both the neurotoxic and hemopathic venoms.

The only antivenin generally available for use in North American countries is a polyvalent Pit Viper antivenin, a product manufactured and sold by one United States pharmaceutical firm, Wyeth Laboratories of Philadelphia. It is reported by the manufacturer, on the basis of the pharmacological and clinical studies done and reported by their research staff and associates, that this new polyvalent Pit Viper antivenin is 50 per cent more effective than previously available antivenins, and that it is capable of neutralizing the venoms of *all* North American Pit Vipers. Numerous experts, however, consider these statements open to debate inasmuch as apparently not all North American Pit Viper venoms were tested.

The antivenin for North American Pit Vipers is formally described as follows* (Fig. 30, p. 117):

> *Antivenin, Polyvalent, Antisnakebite Serum* (Wyeth)
>
> COMPOSITION: Hyperimmune equine serum containing protective substances against Pit Viper venoms.
>
> ACTION AND USES: To prevent death, and to relieve symptoms after snakebite.
>
> ADMINISTRATION AND DOSAGE: Contents of one to five syringes, part injected subcutaneously** or intramuscularly around the wound (if given within the first two hours), and the remainder intramuscularly high on the bitten limb, subcutaneously in the abdominal wall or interscapular region, or, in grave cases, intravenously or intraperitoneally. Repeat injections and continue suction until symptoms subside. In the presence of horse serum allergy, use cautiously, after desensitization.
>
> HOW SUPPLIED. One combination package containing one vial of Antivenin, one syringe of sterile water for injection (U.S.P. with preservative), one vial of Normal Horse Serum 1:10 dilution (for testing patient's sensitivity to horse serum), and one sterile needle.

---

* J. Paul Folsom (Editor): *Physicians' Desk Reference to Specialties and Biologicals.* Oradell, N. J., Medical Economics, Inc., 1956, p. 595.
** We should like to point out that Boquet (1956) has demonstrated that mixture with hyaluronidase, one of the "spreading-factors" normally occurring in snake venoms, is also beneficial in the *subcutaneous* use of antivenin on laboratory animals, greatly increasing the rapidity of dispersal and the recovery rate.

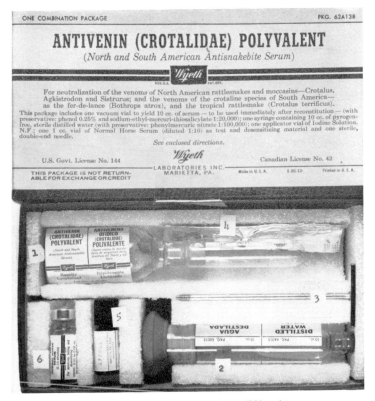

Fig. 30. Antivenin Polyvalent (Wyeth).

1. Antivenin (sterile powder, one dose).
2. Hypodermic syringe, containing 10 cc. of sterile distilled water (for dissolving antivenin powder).
3. Metal handle for moving the plunger of the syringe.
4. Sterile hypodermic needle (inside foil).
5. Small vial of antiseptic.
6. Small vial of normal horse serum (for sensitivity testing, or for desensitization).

There are certain inherent difficulties or disadvantages in using antivenins. Because of these possible complications, the effectiveness of antivenins is always problematical.

1. Antivenins are not always available; they may not be carried in the drug stores of small communities, and hospitals do not always stock them.

However, in most areas of the United States where venomous snakebite cases may occur, many physicians keep a small supply of antivenin on hand, or know where a supply can be secured upon short notice.

2. Another problem is that some people may develop serious anaphylactic reactions to antivenins.

In antivenin therapy one imperative precaution must always be observed, namely, to test the patient for sensitivity to horse serum before administering the antivenin. In this connection, it might be mentioned that each package of antivenin (always a single dose) contains a vial of one cubic centimeter (1 cc.) of normal horse serum 1:10 for testing sensitivity, and presumably for desensitization. The clinical testing for horse serum sensitivity by intradermal wheals is a practical enough procedure. But, when one encounters a case of bite by a poisonous snake wherein the patient is sensitive to horse serum, the practical therapeutic problem presented is a difficult one. As brought out by Shannon (personal communication), presuming that the patient can be fully desensitized (which he doubts), how can it be done fast enough to help the victim? Certainly not by desensitization methods such as used with tetanus antitoxin (TAT). The task of desensitizing patients before proceeding with standard antivenin administration is, in our belief, totally impractical. It is reported (oral communication) that in some areas, as for example Mexico, most individuals are sensitive to horse serum and thus the use of antivenin is seriously curtailed.

3. Despite the statements of some authorities, there is honest difference of opinion among them about the therapeutic value of the *polyvalent* antivenins.

Monovalent Versus Polyvalent Antivenins

Numerous authorities affirm that the only antivenin of value is the monovalent type against a single, specific snake venom. The practical question that always arises is, how can one be certain of the specific identity of the offending snake? It is frequently difficult to be sure whether or not it is a venomous snake, let alone what kind of a poisonous snake it may be. Unless this is known, the use of the monovalent antivenin may be of little or no value. And, too, were a monovalent antivenin employed, it might conceivably be used against the wrong species of snake, and thereby presumably be ineffective.

Maintenance of readily available supplies of a sufficient variety of types of monovalent antivenins is also a serious problem. In reality, monovalent antivenins simply are not easily accessible to most physicians for employment in counteracting the venoms of most species of snakes. Only polyvalent antivenins are practical from the points of view of manufacture and distribution.

Paraspecific Antivenin Immunity with Different Snake Species

The relative effectiveness of monovalent *versus* polyvalent antivenins theoretically hinges upon the degree to which the various species involved share identical poisonous factors in their venoms. The most favorable situation, from the point of view of treatment, would be the complete sharing of all factors by all species. On the contrary, however, the venoms of all species differ somewhat, the degree of difference being more or less proportional to the degree of taxonomic differentiation, with members of different families being the most widely different from each other.

Research reports show, curiously, that the relative effectiveness of monovalent *versus* polyvalent antivenins hinges also upon another factor—the capacity of each factor to produce an antigen by the techniques now utilized in preparation of antivenin. On a theoretical basis, a monovalent antivenin should be expected to be more effective in treatment of bites by the species from which it is prepared than any other antivenin. Yet, as reported by Criley (1956), in practice it has been shown that certain polyvalent antivenins, even without *any* component for a given species, are more effective against the bites of that species than are antivenins prepared in part from venom of the same species. Thus, antigen content of antivenin is not directly proportional to the poison-factor content of the venom, despite theoretical expectation. Criley (*op. cit.*) has demonstrated that the present formula for preparation of polyvalent antivenin, based on a mixture of venoms of only 4 species, is more effective against the bites of these species *and also against those of related species* than was the antivenin formerly prepared with the use of a larger variety of venoms, including those of related species.

The fortune of American physicians in the present connection is that all the species of venomous snakes in the Western Hemisphere, except the Coral Snakes, are sufficiently closely related that antivenin prepared from venom selected from only 4 species can effectively counteract the bites of *apparently* all species (not all have been tested).

A widely circulated supposition exists that antivenins are particularly effective against neurotoxins as opposed to hemopathogens, and that therefore any antivenin (e.g., the anti-Crotalic preparation of Wyeth), in the absence of something more specific, would be useful in the treatment of the bite of any snake with predominantly neurotoxic venom. Minton (personal correspondence) has shown that neither supposition is correct. Antivenin counteracts neurotoxins neither more nor less effectively than it does hemopathogens, and there is little or no sharing of any poisonous fractions in the venoms of snakes of different families. The best procedure in any case is to select for use the antivenin prepared to combat the bites of species identical with, or most closely related to, the species that caused the bite. (See Keegan, 1956, for a world-wide list of antivenins and their capacities).

4. As pointed out by many authorities, a serious error in therapy is said to be the administration of insufficient antivenin.

Minton, an experienced snakebite clinician and therapist, stresses the importance of giving antivenin as early as possible, and in a single dose rather than in divided doses if it is to be used at all. He has expressed doubt as to whether local injections of antivenin around the wound helps much even in the first two hours. A child requires proportionally and actually larger doses than an adult. When indicated, antivenin saves life if administered up to two-thirds of the death time. For example, if the patient has received a dose of venom sufficient to kill in 9 hours, antivenin therapy is effective if given within 6 hours. No case is too advanced to receive antivenin, and even paralyzed patients with involvement of the respiratory muscles may recover if given antivenin in adequate dosage. If respiratory paralysis clears up and then recurs, re-administration of antivenin is indicated.

D.   ANTI-SHOCK MEASURES

In any venomous snakebite case, shock may develop, the degree varying with the extent of the poisoning of the victim. A greater appreciation of the danger of shock in snakebite, as well as better cognizance of the more recent advances in therapy giving better protection against it, account for the major improvements in treatment in recent years.

In snakebite poisoning, the major causes of shock include (a) massive envenomation, (b) release of histamines by the conversion of lecithin to lysolecithin by the lecithinases in the venom, and (c) anaphylaxis. True anaphylaxis is seen in snakebite cases: (1) most frequently in association with sensitivity to the serum in the antivenin, and (2) rarely in association with sensitization of the victim to a particular venom as a result of bites or exposures (see cases cited by Stanic, 1956). It is true, as pointed out by Minton, that some of the symptoms of severe snakebites are similar to those of anaphylaxis, and may depend upon the same basic mechanism, but this is not considered true anaphylaxis.

Specific anti-shock measures available to the physician are as follows.

1. General Measures

Continuation of standard first aid methods for allaying shock: placing the victim in the Trendelenburg position, maintaining normal bodily heat or temperature, psychological reassurance, et cetera.

2. Blood Transfusion

As previously cited in this treatise, one group of enzymes present in many snake venoms is the *cytolysins*, agents that destroy *in vivo* the red blood cells. The red blood cells may become so reduced in number as to be incapable of supplying sufficient quantities of oxygen to the tissues, at which point tissue respiration becomes seriously impaired. When any significant degree of tissue oxygen deficiency occurs, all bodily functions rapidly decline, and death will eventually occur if this erythrocyte deficiency cannot promptly be restored to a semblance of normal levels.

Whole blood transfusion, administered intravenously, quite obviously is the key method for red blood cell replacement. For technical reasons, it usually is impossible to set up blood transfusion in the field; in civilian life the technique requires hospital facilities. That is why any snakebite victim needing blood transfusion should be taken to the nearest hospital with minimal delay, and be blood typed immediately. Transfusion may be required quickly. Blood counts, and related hematological tests, should be made every three hours until hemopathic activity is under control.

3. Other Intravenous Injections

Plasma, 5 per cent dextrose solution, normal saline solution, or Ringer's solution, are acceptable forms of fluid replacements that may be employed instead of, or in conjunction with, whole blood.

4. Miscellaneous Drugs

Special preparations now available, and reported to have some value in treating shock in snakebite cases, are (a) epinephrine, (b) cortisone, (c) ACTH, and (d) antihistamines.

Epinephrine. In snakebite literature, this old standard anti-shock drug apparently has not been found very useful. See Klauber (1956: 896) for a summary of the literature.

Cortisone and ACTH. Schoettler (1954) has reported that these drugs are ineffective in the final outcome of poisonous snakebite cases. Minton (personal communication) has revealed that his own experimental work fully confirms Schoettler's views, but that he (Minton) believes that ACTH and cortisone should have a place in snakebite therapy because (a) they do markedly decrease the violent inflammatory reaction that accompanies poisonous snakebites, they do produce considerable relief from pain, and perhaps do lessen local tissue damage by the venom; and (b) the drugs prevent allergic side reactions caused by either the antivenin or by tetanus antitoxin. Ganatra (1957) also recommends use of hydrocortisone in conjunction with antivenin; he did, however, find that in mice the mortality is reduced 17 per cent with use of hydrocortisone alone.

Antihistamines. Histamines, chemicals formed in the bodily tissues in the shock state, have the property of producing relaxation (vasodilatation) of the capillary walls. When these walls thereby collapse, large amounts of blood collect in the tissue capillary spaces or beds, and so reduce the blood volume in active circulation as to threaten death through tissue asphyxiation and cardiac failure. This is the state of shock.

The antihistamine drugs are given hypodermically with the hope that the abnormally large quantities of histamine released by the venom present in the body will be neutralized, thereby minimizing the development of shock. Theoretically, antihistamines should be highly useful, especially in *neurotoxic* snakebite cases, but in clinical practice the reports seem to be that they have little value in the treatment of North American snakebite. They are reported to be possibly more efficacious combined with heparin (Shannon, 1957: 137). This holds only for neurotoxic cases; in hemopathic cases, the supplemental employment of heparin would merely hasten the bleeding because of its anticoagulant properties. The use of antihistamines *per se* is not believed to do harm, and in serious cases might provide the essential margin for survival.

E. CALCIUM SUPPLEMENTS

The anaphylactic paralysis resulting from hypersensitivity to insect stings is often rather spectacularly alleviated by the use of intravenous calcium gluconate or calcium lactate (Miller, 1956). This treatment is also helpful in combating the painful cramps caused by the bite of the black widow spider (Bogen, 1956). Shannon (1957: 139) points out a use for these drugs in counteracting spasmodic contractions of muscles in the limbs which have become involved and badly swollen in snakebite. Although we have found no literature to substantiate the use of intravenous calcium preparations for snakebite, we suggest that they might well prove extremely helpful especially in counteracting neurotoxic effects.

In fact we do possess oral reports that intravenous injection of 10 per cent calcium gluconate is the standard and basically sole treatment of snakebite employed in at least one large hospital in Puebla, Mexico. We are indebted to Dr. William E. Duellman, a herpetologist of Wayne University, for this information, derived from his own experience in that hospital when treated for snakebite. His physician related that antivenin no longer was the standard treatment at that institution since too large a proportion of the patients at that hospital is sensitive to horse serum. Instead, the basic treatment is with calcium gluconate injected slowly until suppression of the sympathetic nervous system responses becomes marked, whereupon Coramine is injected as a stimulant. This procedure was put into effect about an hour and a half after Dr. Duellman was bitten on the thumb by a rattlesnake (*Crotalus scutulatus*) about 2½ ft. long. No other remedial measures were taken, either before or after calcium gluconate treatment. The bite was fully effective, both fangs entering the digit. Swelling of the hand was moderate by the time treatment was initiated, but no further advancement was noted. Although this species is notorious for its strongly neurotoxic venom, no neurotoxic effects were noted at any time. Recovery was uneventful.

It is accordingly our belief that use of calcium gluconate or calcium lactate warrants serious confirmatory consideration as an important and perhaps even a basic procedure in snakebite therapy.

F.   GLYCINE

White (1957) has pointed out that rattlesnake venom contains a relatively large amount of zinc. He suggests that zinc may comprise an essential part of the toxic enzymes of snake venom in much the same way that it is known to serve as an important component of some of the enzymes (e.g. carbonic anhydrase) of the mammalian body. Since glycine has a strong affinity for zinc, he proposes a highly interesting hypothesis that glycine might prove to be an effective neutralizing agent for venom in snakebite cases. Preliminary experiments are said to bear out this hypothesis.

G.   NEOSTIGMINE

Another drug reported by some (e.g., Shannon, 1956: 407) to have some value in selected snakebite cases is neostigmine. Since it is an anti-cholinesterase, it may produce some benefit (certainly theoretical) by combating neurotoxins found in certain venomous snakes, mainly the poisonous Coral Snakes and exotic members of the same family as well as Sea Snakes. In neurotoxic venoms, the enzyme cholinesterase is abundant and accounts for much of the toxicity produced by them. At the myoneural junctions it breaks down the hormone acetylcholine, in turn essential for normal nerve activity or function. The value of neostigmine is that it neutralizes the cholinesterase.

Despite the theoretical soundness for the employment of neostigmine in neurotoxic snakebite cases, it has not as yet been used in a sufficient number of cases to reveal its real value in snakebite therapy. The drug should be considered, however, in any case exhibiting extreme neurotoxic involvement. Shannon recommends an intravenous injection of a *test dose* of 2 mg. of neostigmine methylsulfate and 0.6 mg. of atropine sulfate. If a favorable response ensues, he recommends repetition of the same 2.0 mg. intravenous dose of neostigmine methylsulfate (but no atropine) one-half hour after the initial dose, with a follow-up to 15.0 mg. tablets of neostigmine methylsulfate as indicated.

H.   ASCORBIC ACID

Corkill (1956) has, in his practice in Africa, come to the conclusion that ascorbic acid (Vitamin C) deficiency and hemopathogens are synergistic since both produce hemorrhages from mucous membranes. In Corkill's medical practice, handling many cases of significant malnutrition, he employed with success one gram doses daily of ascorbic acid for the duration of the recovery period in all snakebite cases. Undoubtedly an ascorbic acid supplement would prove beneficial as a standard treatment in all cases of severe snakebite under circumstances of real malnutrition.

I.   SEDATION

In any snakebite case, poisonous or non-poisonous, whenever undue anxiety is present, the use of some standard sedative drug is to be considered. Whenever sedatives are employed in snakebite cases, they should be used with care, and never in such quantities as to mask symptoms and thereby handicap the physician in following the true clinical course of the case. Since narcotics are synergistic with neurotoxin, they or drugs of similar physiological effects should be used with great caution and avoided completely in case of doubt.

As for the possible place of the new atractic or "tranquilizer" drugs in the treatment of poisonous snakebite cases, on general principles they should be expected to prove helpful, especially in not too severe cases showing acute anxiety. However, as has been indicated to us by Minton (personal communication), since few or no reports have yet appeared in the literature revealing how the "tranquilizer" drugs act upon persons suffering from severe snakebite poisoning, and since some of these drugs produce a considerable drop in blood pressure (which could aggravate the shock state likely present), they must be used with great caution until more is known about their effects.

J.   ARTIFICIAL RESPIRATION

When respiratory movements become alarmingly depressed, and/or actual respiratory paralysis occurs, it is recommended that artificial respiration be instituted (either by an accepted resuscitator machine, or by an accepted manual technique), and that oxygen be given simultaneously. Artificial respiration actually can give but little or no therapeutic help in respiratory paralysis due to snake venom poisoning since it does not counteract the cause—namely, the high concentration of cholinesterase at the nerve endings which inhibits or depresses normal nerve cell function. However, Shannon and others consider artificial respiration harmless, and worth a try in marginal cases.

K. ANTIBIOTICS

Septicemia is more than a usual threat in snakebite cases, both because of organisms introduced from the snake's mouth, and because of the antibactericidal properties of snake venom. Medical case reports (e.g., Parrish, 1956) demonstrate that the mouths and venom glands of North American Pit Vipers contain innumerable bacteria, some of which but not all are harmful when introduced into the tissues of snakebite victims. Certainly serious infection may likely develop after snakebite if antibacterial medication is not given promptly. Antibiotics may be used in precautionary doses, or as needed by developments in the individual clinical case.

It is also recommended by clinicians that tetanus and gas gangrene antisera be given, either separately or combined with antibiotic therapy.

L. PURGATIVES

Because in the past some authors have reported that in severe snakebite cases some venom may be eliminated from the victim's system *via* the intestinal tract, several herpetological sources recommend use of mild purgatives and/or gentle colonic irrigations (e.g., with saline solution). Whether or not some snake venom is eliminated *via* the intestinal tract, as pointed out to us by Shannon, efforts to employ purgatives or colonic irrigations in any snakebite case are objectionable on two scores. *First*, there are no truly authoritative case reports in the scientific literature about venom being removed from the intestinal tract by such measures. *Secondly*, even if the venom were thus removable, such practice is still considered objectionable because purgatives and/or colonic irrigations may aggravate intestinal hemorrhage already initiated in snakebite cases by hemopathic venoms.

M. ANTIPRURITICS

Sometimes when antivenins are employed in the treatment of venomous snakebite cases, the victim develops severe itching of the skin associated with drug sensitivity. In such instances, various drugs known to lessen or ameliorate itching (e.g., Benedryl) are recommended. On the other hand the best treatment of itching is its prophylaxis. The more carefully that all recommended precautions regarding the use of the potentially lifesaving but dangerous antivenin are observed, the smaller will be the number of cases with itching.

N. DIET AND LIQUIDS

A liquid or bland diet for the first few days, especially in dangerous cases, is advised. Later on blood-building foods, with supplemental injections of liver concentrates, are recommended. Water consumption should be encouraged. Since kidney damage is not an infrequent complication in venomous snakebite cases, frequent urine analyses are desirable so that appropriate medical therapy may be instituted as necessary.

O. CRYOTHERAPY (Local Tissue Refrigeration)

Periodically in recent years, especially in the popular press, the method of cryotherapy has been recommended for use in the treatment of cases of venomous snakebite. The commonly suggested devices for effecting refrigeration of the tissues at or adjacent to the bite area are ethyl chloride spray, ice packs, cold water packs, et cetera. Despite the statements of its advocates (e.g., Stahnke *et al.*, 1957), the most carefully documented clinical case reports, such as those recently published by Shannon (1956: 408-412), make it abundantly clear that cryotherapeutic techniques applied to snake bites are strongly contraindicated. They are known in several cases to have had severely detrimental effects, because tissues are in fact destroyed or predisposed to become gangrenous if refrigerated.

P. CONTINUED CARE

It cannot be overemphasized that great variability of prognosis is attendant upon snakebite. The closest vigilance for at least 48 to 72 hours is required routinely in most serious cases, and longer of course if the symptoms or case history so indicate. Spectacular hemorrhagic symptoms may clear rapidly, only to be replaced by much more insidious and dangerous neurotoxic symptoms that can result in death before aid can be summoned. Even in recent years patients have been reported to have been medically released after alleviation of hemorrhagic symptoms only to have them succumb shortly thereafter to neurotoxic effects. The need for supportive measures against shock or neurotoxins may arise suddenly and unexpectedly at any time within the first 72 hours, and occasionally after even longer intervals up to two weeks or more. In cases of snakebite from some species (e.g., the Florida Diamondback Rattlesnake), the most crucial period is said to fall between the 3rd and 6th day.

BIBLIOGRAPHY

1. Ahuja, M. L., and Gurkirpal Singh: "Snakebite in India," in *Venoms*—AAAS Publication No. 44, edited by Eleanor E. Buckley and Nandor Porges. Washington, D. C., American Association for the Advancement of Science, 1956, pp. 341-351.

2. Amaral, Afranio do: "Snake Venation (Ophidism)," in *Clinical Tropical Medicine,* edited by R. B. H. Gradwohl, L. B. Soto, and O. Felsenfeld. St. Louis, C. V. Mosby Company, 1951, Chapter 57, pp. 1238-1264.

3. American Red Cross: *First Aid Textbook.* Washington, D. C., American National Red Cross, 1957, pp. 148-151. (This is the latest revision.)
   This is the most widely used first aid text in the United States, and covers in brief but practical fashion the general information that first aiders need to know concerning the identification of venomous snakes, signs and symptoms associated with bites by poisonous snakes, precautions against snakebites, and first aid treatment in snakebite cases.

4. Anonymous: *Antivenin.* Philadelphia. Wyeth Laboratories, Inc., 1951, 19 pages.
   A valuable pamphlet, not only on the use of antivenin, but also for its discussion of first aid and hospital measures in the treatment of snakebite cases.

5. Beckman, Harry: *Treatment in General Practice.* Philadelphia, W. B. Saunders Company, 1943, pp. 858-860. Same general information covered as in Reference 3, except that it is discussed on a more professional plane. In addition, antivenin therapy receives practical consideration.

6. Bogen, Emil: "The Treatment of Spider Bite Poisoning," in *Venoms*—AAAS Publication No. 44, edited by Eleanor E. Buckley and Nandor Porges. Washington,

D. C., American Association for the Advancement of Science, 1956, pp. 101-105.

7. Bogert, Charles M., and Rafael Martin del Campo: "The Gila Monster and Its Allies." *Bulletin of the American Museum of Natural History*, 109:1-238, 1956.

8. Boquet, P.: *Venins de Serpents et Antivenins*. Paris Éditions Médicalés Flammarion, 1948, 157 pages.

9. Boquet, P.: "Effect of Hyaluronidase on the Therapeutic activity of Antivenoms," in *Venoms*—AAAS Publication No. 44, edited by Eleanor E. Buckley and Nandor Porges. Washington, D. C., American Association for the Advancement of Science, 1956, pp. 387-391.

10. Buckley, Eleanor E., and Nandor Porges (Editors): *Venoms*—AAAS Publication No. 44, Washington, D. C., American Association for the Advancement of Science, 1956, 467 pages.

11. Cole, Warren C. and Charles B. Puestow: *First Aid: Surgical and Medical*. New York, Appleton-Century-Crofts, 1951, pp. 88-90.
Same as for Reference 5.

12. Corkill, Norman L.: "Snake Poisoning in the Sudan," in *Venoms*—AAAS Publication No. 44, edited by Eleanor E. Buckley and Nandor Porges. Washington, D. C., American Association for the Advancement of Science, 1956, pp. 331-339.

13. Criley, B. R.: "Development of a Multivalent Antivenin for the Family Crotalidae," in *Venoms*—AAAS Publication No. 44, edited by Eleanor E. Buckley and Nandor Porges. Washington, D. C., American Association for the Advancement of Science, 1956, pp. 373-380.

14. Crimmins, M. L.: "The Treatment of Poisonous Snakebite in Texas." *Proceedings and Transactions of the Texas Academy of Science*, 29:54-61, 1946.
An exposition of the incision-suction method developed by Dr. Dudley Jackson of San Antonio, Texas. It in-

cludes a description of the "Dudley" snakebite first aid kit, with instructions regarding its employment.

15. Curran, C. H., and Carl Kauffeld: *Snakes and Their Ways.* New York, Harper and Brothers Publishers, 1937, 285 pages.
    Worldwide in scope. An excellent summary of habits and of snakes in history and religion.

16. Davis, Henry T., and C. S. Brimley: *Poisonous Snakes of the Eastern United States, with First Aid Guide.* Raleigh, N. C., North Carolina State Museum, 1944, 16 pages.

17. DeCoursey, Russell M.: *The Human Organism.* New York, McGraw-Hill Book Company, 1955, p. 288.

18. *Encyclopaedia Britannica.* Chicago, Encyclopaedia Britannica, Inc., 1947 edition, pp. 849-853.
    Mostly concerned with the zoological classification and description of various species of snakes (poisonous and non-poisonous). This article also includes brief discussion about standard first aid measures against venomous snakes and about medical measures (including antivenin therapy) for employment in such cases.

19. Fitzsimons, F. W.: *The Snakes of South Africa: Their Venom and the Treatment of Snake Bite.* Blackwell, Oxford, England, 1921, 550 pages.
    A remarkably thorough account of venomous snakes and the action and treatment of their bites; written by one of the earliest students and producers of antivenin.

20. Fulton, John F. (Editor): *A Textbook of Physiology.* Philadelphia, W. B. Saunders Company, 1949, p. 543. Discussion of blood coagulation caused by snake venoms.

21. Ganatra, R. D., *et al.*: "Use of Hydrocortisone in Experimental Viper Venom Poisoning in Mice." *Indian Journal of Medical Sciences,* 11:493-495, 1957.
    Hydrocortisone by itself reduces mortality in mice by

17%. Use of hydrocortisone with antivenin is recommended.

22. Ganguli, S. K., and L. E. Napier: "Snakes and Snake-bite," in *Principles and Practice of Tropical Medicine*, edited by L. E. Napier. London, Macmillan Company, 1946, pp. 836-859.

23. Ghosh, B. N., and N. K. Sarkar: "Active Principles of Snake Venoms," in *Venoms*—AAAS Publication No. 44, edited by Eleanor E. Buckley and Nandor Porges. Washington, D. C., American Association for the Advancement of Science, 1956, pp. 189-196.

24. Gingrich, W. C., and J. C. Hohenadel: "Standardization of Polyvalent Antivenin," in *Venoms*—AAAS Publication No. 44, edited by Eleanor E. Buckley and Nandor Porges. Washington, D. C., American Association for the Advancement of Science, 1956, pp. 381-385.

25. Gloyd, Howard K.: "The Problem of Too Many Snakes." *Chicago Naturalist*, 7:87-97, 1944.

26. Halstead, Bruce W.: "Animal Phyla Known to Contain Poisonous Marine Animals," in *Venoms*—AAAS Publication No. 44, edited by Eleanor E. Buckley and Nandor Porges. Washington, D. C., American Association for the Advancement of Science, 1956, pp. 9-27.

27. Harmon, R. W. and C. B. Pollard: *Bibliography of Animal Venoms*. Gainesville, University of Florida Press, 1949, 40 pages.

28. Henderson, John: *First Aid*. New York, Bantam Book F-1365, 1955, pp. 218-222.
Same information as Reference 3.

29. Keegan, Hugh L.: "Antivenins Available for Treatment of Envenomation by Poisonous Snakes, Scorpions, and Spiders," in *Venoms*—AAAS Publication No. 44, edited by Eleanor E. Buckley and Nandor Porges, Washington, D. C., American Association for the Advancement of Science, 1956, pp. 413-438.

30. Klauber, Laurence M.: *Rattlesnakes: Their Habits, Life History, and Influence on Mankind.* Berkeley, University of California Press, 1956, 2 volumes, 1476 pages.

31. Leake, Chauncey D.: "Development of Knowledge About Venoms," in *Venoms*—AAAS Publication No. 44, edited by Eleanor E. Buckley and Nandor Porges. Washington, D. C., American Association for the Advancement of Science, 1956, pp. 1-4.

32. Lee, Chen-Yuan, Chuan-Chiung Chang, and Kazuya Kamijo: "Cholinesterase Inactivating Activity of Snake Venom," in *Venoms*—AAAS Publication No. 44, edited by Eleanor E. Buckley and Nandor Porges. Washington, D. C., American Association for the Advancement of Science, 1956, p. 197.

33. Loeb, Leo, *et al: The Venom of Heloderma.* Washington, D. C., Carnegie Publication No. 177, 1913, 224 pages.

34. Miller, D. G.: "Massive Anaphylaxis from Insect Stings," in *Venoms*—AAAS Publication No. 44, edited by Eleanor E. Buckley and Nandor Porges. Washington, D. C., American Association for the Advancement of Science, 1956, pp. 117-121.

35. Minton, Sherman A.: "Injuries by Venomous Animals in Indiana." *Proceedings of the Indiana Academy of Science, 60:*315-323, 1950.
    Discussion of bites by various venomous animals, including snakes. Detailed case studies of reported poisonous snakebite cases in Indiana 1930-1950, with review of etiological factors in each case, and evaluation of acceptable first aid and medical therapy.

36. Minton, Sherman A.: "Polyvalent Antivenin in the Treatment of Experimental Snake Venom Poisoning." *American Journal of Tropical Medicine and Hygiene, 3:*1077-1082, 1954.

37. Minton, Sherman A.: "Snakebite." *Scientific American, 196:*114-118, 120, 122, 1957.

38. Moore, Robert A.: *A Textbook of Pathology*. Philadelphia, W. B. Saunders Company, 1944, pp. 605-606.
    Brief but professional discussion of tissue changes, local and systematic, in cases of venomous snakebite; nature of snake venom.

39. Oliver, James A.: "Snakes and Snake Poisoning," in *Clinical Tropical Medicine*, edited by Z. T. Bercovitz. New York, P. B. Hoeber Company, 1944, Chapter 66, pp. 855-880.

40. Oliver, James A.: "The Prevention and Treatment of Snakebite," Animal Kingdom, *Bulletin of the New York Zoological Society, 55*:66-83, 1952.

41. Oliver, James A. and Leonard J. Goss: "Antivenin Available for the Treatment of Snakebite." *Copeia*, volume (none), 270-272, 1952.

42. Oliver, James A.: *The Natural History of North American Amphibians and Reptiles*. Princeton, D. Van Nostrand Company, 1955, 359 pages.

43. Parrish, Henry M., A. W. Maclaurin, and Robert L. Tuttle: "North American Pit Vipers, Bacterial Flora of the Mouths and Venom Glands." *Virginia Medical Monthly, 83*:383-385, 1956.

44. Parrish, Henry M., J. E. Scatterday, and C. B. Pollard: "The Clinical Management of Snake Venom Poisoning in Domestic Animals." *Journal of the American Veterinary Medicine Association, 130*:548-551, 1957.
    First aid: tourniquet, incision, suction; medical treatment: the 'three A's'—antivenin, antibiotics, antitoxin; cortisone and ACTH may prolong life but do not affect mortality rate; epinephrine hydrochloride, meperidine hydrochloride (Demerol), calcium gluconate, intravenous solutions, blood transfusions, may prove beneficial; L-C method (ligature-cryotherapy) rejected.

45. Parrish, Henry M.: "Early Excision and Suction of Snakebite Wounds in Dogs," in *Venoms*—AAAS Publication No. 44, edited by Eleanor E. Buckley and Nandor

Porges. Washington, D. C., American Association for the Advancement of Science, 1956, pp. 399-404.

46. Pope, Clifford H. and R. Marlin Perkins: "Differences in the Patterns of Bites of Venomous and Harmless Snakes." *Archives of Surgery*, *49*:331-336, 1944.

47. Pope, Clifford H.: *The Reptile World*. New York, Alfred A. Knopf, Inc., 1955, 326 pages.
    The most recent, comprehensive and popular treatise on all groups of snakes and other reptiles in the world, with emphasis upon the kinds of the United States. A reliably sound account by a specialist of world-wide fame and experience.

48. St. John Ambulance Association: *First Aid to the Injured*. London, St. John Ambulance Association, 1950, pp. 264-267.
    Same information as Reference 3.

49. Schmidt, Karl P.: *The Truth About Snake Stories*. Chicago, Chicago Natural History Museum, Zoological Booklet No. 10, 1951, 23 pages.

50. Schoettler, W. H. A.: "Antihistamine, ACTH, Cortisone, Hydrocortisone and Anesthetics in Snake Bite." *American Journal of Tropical Medicine and Hygiene*, *3*:1083-1091, 1954.

51. Selye, Hans: *The Physiology and Pathology of Exposure to Stress*. Montreal, Acta Endocrinologica, 1950, pp. 323, 449, 508.
    Brief discussion of the General Adaptation Syndrome in Snakebite cases, mechanism of tissue hemorrhage caused by snake venoms, and toxic effects of venom upon the vascular endothelium in snakebite cases.

52. Shannon, Frederick A.: "Case Reports of Two Gila Monster Bites." *Herpetologia*, *9*:125-127, 1953.

53. Shannon, Frederick A.: "Comments on the Treatment of Reptile Poisoning in the Southwest." *Southwestern Medicine*, *34*:367-373, 1953.

54. Shannon, Frederick A.: *Current Therapy.* Philadelphia, W. B. Saunders Company, 1955, pp. 634-635.
Discusses general supportive treatment, first aid measures, and antivenin medical therapy in handling venomous snakebite cases.

55. Shannon, Frederick A.: "Comments on the Treatment of Reptile Poisoning," in *Venoms*—AAAS Publication No. 44, edited by Eleanor E. Buckley and Nandor Porges. Washington, D. C., American Association for the Advancement of Science, 1956, pp. 405-412.

56. Shannon, Frederick A.: "Treatment of Envenomization by Animals." *Arizona Medicine, 14*:136-142, 1957 (March).

57. Shilling, Charles: *The Human Machine.* Annapolis, United States Naval Institute Publication, 1955, pp. 184-185.
Same information as Reference 3.

58. Smith, Hobart M.: *Snakes as Pets.* All-Pets Books, Inc., 1953, 50 pages.

59. Smith, Hobart M., and Floyd Boys: "Snake Venoms: Hemorrhagic, Hematoxic or Hemopathic?" *Herpetologica, 13*:101-102, 1957.

60. Smith, Philip W.: "Some Facts About Illinois Snakes and Their Control," *Biological Notes No. 32,* Natural History Survey Division, Department of Registration and Education, State of Illinois, Springfield, Illinois, 1953, 8 pages.
General article on the value and harm, occurrence, identification, and control of snakes.

61. Stahnke, H. L., R. M. Allen, R. V. Horan, and J. H. Tenery: "The Treatment of Snakebite." *American Journal of Tropical Medicine, 6*:323-335, 1957.

62. Stanic, Mirko: "Allergenic Properties of Venom Hypersensitiveness in Man and Animals"—in *Venoms*, AAAS Publication No. 44, edited by Eleanor E. Buckley and Nandor Porges. Washington, D. C., American Associ-

ation for the Advancement of Science, 1956, pp. 181-188.

63. Stickel, William H.: "Venomous Snakes of the United States and Treatment of Their Bites." *U. S. Department of the Interior Fish and Wildlife Service, Wildlife Leaflet No. 339*, pp. 1-29, 1952.

64. Stickel, William H.: "Control of Snakes." *U. S. Department of the Interior, Fish and Wildlife Service, Wildlife Leaflet No. 345*, pp. 1-8, 1953.

65. Swaroop, S., and B. Grab: "The Snakebite Mortality Problem in the World," in *Venoms*—AAAS Publication No. 44, edited by Eleanor E. Buckley and Nandor Porges. Washington, D. C., American Association for the Advancement of Science, 1956, pp. 439-446.

66. Tinkham, Ernest R.: "The Deadly Nature of Gila Monster Venom," in *Venoms*—AAAS Publication No. 44, edited by Eleanor E. Buckley and Nandor Porges. Washington, D. C., American Association for the Advancement of Science, 1956, pp. 59-63.

67. Watt, H. F., H. M. Parrish, and C. B. Pollard: "Repeated Poisonous Snakebites in the Same Patient: An Unusual Case Report." *North Carolina Medical Journal, 17*:174-179, 1956.

68. Werler, John E.: "The Poisonous Snakes of Texas, and the First Aid Treatment of Their Bites." *Texas Game and Fish*, Volume (none): 1-16, 1950.

69. White, Fred N.: "Radiation in Venom." *Forum* (University of Houston), *1*(2):16-18, 1957.

70. Wood, John T.: "A Survey of 200 Cases of Snakebite in Virginia." *American Journal of Tropical Medicine and Hygiene, 3*:936-943, 1954.

71. Wood, John T., W. W. Hoback, and T. W. Green: "Treatment of Snake Venom Poisoning with ACTH and Cortisone." *Virginia Medical Monthly, 82*:130-135, 1955.

72. Young, Nettie: "Snakebite: Treatment and Nursing Care." *American Journal of Nursing*, *40*:657-660, 1940. A valuable exposition of the nursing methods used in the hospital by Dr. Dudley Jackson of San Antonio, Texas.

73. Zimmerman, Arnold A. and Clifford H. Pope: "Development and Growth of the Rattle of Rattlesnakes." *Fieldiana* (*Zoology*), *32*:355-413, 1948.

POSTSCRIPT

The continued, periodic appearance in the popular, semi-popular and even the professional literature of vehement denials of the value of the mechanical mode of snakebite treatment (tourniquet application, multiple incisions, and suction) is highly disturbing. We have three pertinent convictions. (1) Proof of the truly great value of mechanical treatment was furnished, in a form generally accepted as incontrovertible, over 30 years ago by Dr. Dudley Jackson (Jackson, D.: "First Aid Treatment for Snakebite," *Texas State Journal of Medicine, 23*:203, 1927; Jackson, D., and W. T. Harrison: "Mechanical Treatment of Experimental Rattlesnake Venom Poisoning," *Journal of the American Medical Association, 90*:1928-9, 1928; Jackson, D., and T. S. Githens: "Treatment of Crotalus Atrox Venom Poisoning in Dogs," *Bulletin of the Antivenin Institute of America, 5*:1-6, 1931). Since then corroboration has been provided again and again by many zoologists and physicians (see Clifford H. Pope, and L. W. Peterson: "Treatment of Poisoning with Rattlesnake Venom. Experiments with Negative Pressure, Tourniquet and Bulb Suction," *Archives of Surgery, 53*:564-569, 1946; Parrish, 1956; and Parrish, Scatterday and Pollard, 1957). This method has certain obvious limitations, of course, but presently it does represent a basic therapeutic approach. (2) Antivenin may be improved in the future and thereby become a panacea for snakebite treatment. However, for reasons discussed on pages 117-121 of this monograph, antivenin therapy as now practiced is seriously limited by practical factors pertaining either to the antivenin itself or to the bitten subject. (3) Finally, on the basis of present knowledge, both antivenin and mechanical therapies have important places in snakebite treatment.

INDEX

A

ACTH, use in snakebite, 123-124
After-effects, snakebite, 60
Alcohol, snakebite, 89
Alligators, 6
Amphibia
  first aid treatment, 11
  location of poison, 7
  modes of poisoning, 7
  nature of poison, 8
  poisonous species of North
    America, 9
  recognition of first aid emer-
    gency, 11
Amphisbaenia, 6
Anaphylaxis, antivenin, 118
Anaphylaxis, venom, 122
Antibiotics, use in snakebite, 129
Antihistamines, use in snakebite,
    124-125
Antipruritics, use in snakebite, 130
Antiseptics, use of
  in Gila Monster bites, 18
  in snakebite, 67, 95-96
Antivenins, snakebite, 114-121, 131
Anura, 5
Anxiety, snakebite, 89, 107
Apoda, 5
Artificial respiration
  use in snakebite, 111, 128
Ascorbic acid, use in snakebite,
    126-127

B

Beaded Lizard, see lizards
Bite pattern, snakebite, 84-85
Bladder, snakes, 32-33

Blood clotting time, diagnostic
  value in snakebite, 108
Body temperature, snakes, 32
Boomslang, 109
Breeding, snakes, 33

C

Caecilians, 5
Caimans, 6
Calcium, use in snakebite, 125-126
Case situations in snakebite,
  recommended first aid proce-
    dure, 99-105
Caudata, 5
Chelonia, see Turtles
Classification
  amphibians, 5
  reptiles, 5-6
Clothing, protection in snakebite,
    64
Cold, use in snakebite, 96, 130-131
Color patterns, skin
  Coral Snakes, 75-76
  Pit Vipers, 74
Colubridae, 42
Common snakes, 42
Control, snakes, 70-71
Copperhead snakes
  lethal doses of venom, 56
  prognosis in bites, 58
  recognition, 76
Copulation, snakes, 33
Coral snakes, 39, 41, 59, 74-76
Corralline snakes, 42
Cortisone, use in snakebite, 123-124
Cottonmouth snakes
  lethal doses of venom, 56

prognosis in bites, 58
recognition, 77
Crocodilia, 6
Crotalidae, 42
Cryotherapy, use in snakebite,
    96, 130-131

D

Death, causes of
    Gila Monster bites, 17
    snakebites, 59
    toad poisoning, 8
    turtle poisoning, 12
Deglutition, snakes, 34-35
Diet, snakes, 33
Diet, in snakebite cases, 130
Digitalis, 8
Drugs, use in snakebite, 106-107,
    110, 123-130

E

Ears, snakes, 30
Elapidae, 42
Envenomation
    lizards, 16
    snakes, 43-44
Epinephrine, in toad poison, 8
Epinephrine, use in snakebite, 123
Erroneous beliefs, snakes, 35-39
Excision, use in snakebite, 113-114
Eyes, snakes, 30-31

F

Fables, snake, 35-39
Fangs
    Gila Monster, 16
    snakes, 26-29, 43, 72
Fear, snakebite, 89, 107
First aid
    amphibian poisoning, 11
    chelonia poisoning, 13-14
    frog poisoning, 11

Gila Monster bites, 17-19
snakebites, 88-105
toad poisoning, 11
turtle poisoning, 13-14
First aid kits, for snakebite, 64-69
Food, use in snakebite, 89-90
Frogs
    classification, 5
    edibility, 8-9
    first aid, 11
    modes of poisoning, 7-8
    nature of poison in poisonous
        species, 8-9
    poisonous species of North
        America, 9-11

G

Gila Monster, see Lizards
Glycine, use in snakebite, 126

H

Head shape, snakes, 81
Hemopathic, response to snake
    venom, 48-50, 52-54
Hemorrhagic, response to snake
    venom, 48
Hemotoxic, response to snake
    venom, 48
Heparin, use in snakebite, 124
Hydrophiidae, 42

I

Incisions
    instruments, 67-68
    precautions, 95-96, 113
    use in reptile bites, 93-96
Immunity, against snake venom,
    69-70
Invertebrates, venoms, 4

K

Kerosene, use in snakebite, 106
Kidney function tests, diagnostic
    value in snakebite, 108

L

Lacertilia, see Lizards
Lethal doses, snakebites, 56-57
Liquids, in snakebite cases, 130
Lizards
  action of venom, 16
  classification, 6
  first aid treatment, 17-19
  kinds, 15
  medical treatment, 19-20
  mode of envenomation, 16
Locomotion, snakes, 22
Lymphatics and venom spread,
  snakes, 90-92

M

Mechanical removal of venom,
  snakebite, 90-98, 111-114
Mechanical treatment *versus* antivenin treatment, in snakebite,
  115, 143
Medical treatment
  frog poisoning, 11
  Gila Monster bites, 19-20
  snakebite, 106-131
  toad poisoning, 11
  turtle poisoning, 14
Moccasins, see Copperhead or
  Cottonmouth snakes
Morbidity, snakebite cases, 50-53,
  85-87
Mortality, snakebite cases, 57-59
Mouth suction, snakebite, 96-97
Myths about snakes, see Fables,
  snakes

N

Neostigmine, use in snakebite,
  126-127
Neurotoxic, response to snake
  venom, 48-52
Newts, 5
Noises, snakes, 83

O

Ophidia, 6
Ophidia, see separate entries under
  snakes, Coral snakes, Pit Vipers,
  etc.
Over-treatment, snakebite, 113

P

Pain, snakebite, 85-86
Paratoid gland, 10
Physical activity, snakebite cases,
  89
Pits, snakes, 32
Pit Vipers, 39-41, 57-59, 72-74,
  77-82
Poisoning
  Amanita muscaria, 13-14
  Amanita phalloides, 13-14
  amphibia, 7-8
  frog, 11
  lizards, 16-20
  mushroom, 13-14
  snakes, see Snakes
  toad, 11
  turtle, 13-14
Poisons
  amphibian, 8
  turtles, 13
  vertebrates, 4
Position, bodily, snakebite, 88-89
Potassium permanganate, use in
  snakebite, 96, 106
Potency of venomous snakebite,
  variables, 54-56
Precautions, against snakebite,
  61-71
Prognosis, in snakebites, 57-58, 131
Purgatives, use in snakebite, 129
Psychotherapy, snakebite, 107

R

Rattles, 23-25, 73
Rattlesnakes
  identification, 74, 77-83

lethal doses in snakebite, 56
prognosis in Rattlesnake bites,
   57-59
Recognition of poisonous snakes,
   72-83
Recognition of poisonous snakebites, 83-87
Refrigeration, use in snakebite, 96,
   130-131
Relapse, snakebite sequel, 131
Remedies, rejected in snakebite,
   96, 106-107
Respiration
   artificial, use in snakebite,
      111, 128
   snakes, 32
Rhynchocephalia, 5

S

Salamanders, 5, 7
Scale patterns, under-surface of
   snake tail, 81
Sea snakes, 42
Sedation, use in snakebite, 127-128
Sensitivity to antivenin, 118, 122
Sensitivity to venom, 122
Shock, treatment in snakebite,
   121-125
Size
   Gila Monsters, 15
   snakes, 21
Skeletal system, snakes, 21
Skin, snakes, 22-23
Skin color patterns, snakes, 73-80
Snake noises, 83
Snakes, recognition of poisonous,
   72-83
Snakes, see separate entries
Snakebite
   case situations, recommended
      first aid procedure, 99-105
   diagnosis, 108-109
   kits, first aid, 64-69

recognition of poisonous, 83-87
remedies, rejected, 96, 106-107
Spreading factor, snake venom,
   113
Squamata, 6
Suction, in reptile bites, 68-69,
   96-98, 111-114
Surgical measures, snakebite,
   86-87, 109
Swallowing, snakes, 34-35
Swelling, local tissue, snakebite,
   86-87, 109
Symptomatology, snakebite, 84-87

T

Tail, snakes, use in identification,
   81-82
Teeth
   Gila Monster, 16
   snakes, 25
Terrapins, 5
Toads
   classification, 5, 7
   edibility, 8-9
   poisonous species of North
      America, 9-11
Tobacco, use in snakebite, 106
Tongue, snakes, 31
True Vipers, 42
Tortoises, 5
Tourniquet
   description, 66
   precautions, 92-93
   use in snakebite, 92-93
Transfusion, blood
   use in snakebite, 122-123
Tranquilizers, use in snakebite, 128
Tuatara, 5
Turpentine, use in snakebite, 106
Turtles
   classification, 5
   first aid, 13-14
   nature of poison, 13
   poisonous species, 12

V

Venom actions
  lizards, 16
  snakes, 48-54
Venom composition
  lizards, 16
  snakes, 45-48
Venom spread, snakes, 44-45,
  90-92
Venomous, defined, 3
Venomous snakes, kinds, 39-42
Venoms
  invertebrate, 4
  vertebrate, 4

Vertebrates
  poisonous, 4
  venomous, 4
Viperidae, 42

W

Walking, hazard in snakebite,
  61-64
Warts, 7

Z

Zinc, use for detoxification
  of snake venom, 126